From the Editors of *The Mailbox* magazine

The February/March Activity Book

Editors:
Becky Andrews
Diane Badden
Lynn Bemer
Irving Crump
Sarah McCutcheon
Karen Shelton
Kathy Wolf

Artist:
Marilynn G. Barr

Cover Design:
Pam Crane

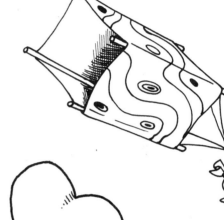

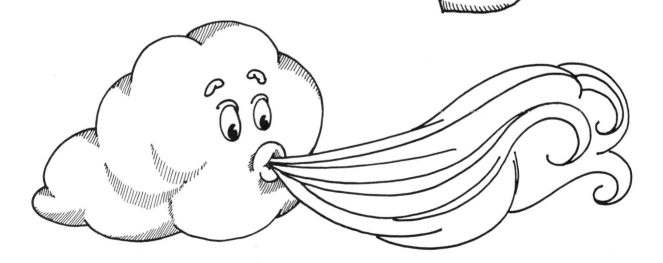

Table Of Contents

How To Use This Book.. 4

National Children's Dental Health Month 5–14

Groundhog Day 15–19

Valentine's Day 20–44

Black History Month 45–52

Presidents' Day 53–62

St. Patrick's Day 63–77

Spring 78–97

Birds 98–107

National Nutrition Month 108–112

Butterflies 113–122

Seasonal Clip Art 123–125

Answer Keys 126–128

How To Use This Book

The *February/March Activity Book* provides you with exciting learning activities for the holidays and special celebrations of February and March. On these pages we've included teacher-tested bulletin boards, art activities, patterns, class activities, learning centers, worksheets, clever clip art, and more.

The book is organized around thematic units. You'll find multidisciplinary units on such seasonal topics as Valentine's Day, Black History Month, St. Patrick's Day, and Spring. We've also featured fun units on National Children's Dental Health Month, Groundhog Day, Presidents' Day, birds, butterflies, and more. All of the ideas can be used independently if you choose not to use a unit approach.

Helpful Tips

- Make notations about each unit (page numbers, types of reproducibles, etc.) on a small index card. Tape the cards to your monthly idea files for February and March as reminders to include the units in your planning.

- If a worksheet is too difficult or too easy for your students, white-out the programming and write in your own problems and new directions with a black, fine-tipped marker. You may also change problems or directions by masking type with white paper and making a photocopy for duplication.

- To use the clip art pages, duplicate a copy of each page. When you want to decorate a student worksheet, parent communication, class newsletter, or award, cut out the appropriate artwork and attach it to the page before making your photocopies.

- Extend the use of smaller patterns to make nametags, awards, and badges. Or have students trace the patterns to make cutouts for you to program with skills.

Brushing Up On Dental Health

February is National Children's Dental Health Month, the perfect time to brush up on important dental health concepts. Encourage your students to sport healthy smiles with the following creative tips, activities, and reproducibles.

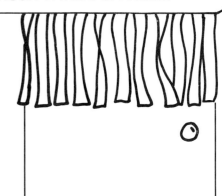

HAPPY SMILES BRUSH THROUGH HERE!

Happy Smiles Brush Through Here

Greet your students with a giant toothbrush door decoration to announce your dental health studies. For bristles, cut white plastic garbage bags into strips and tape to the top of your classroom door frame. Cut out bulletin board paper to complete a giant toothbrush. Students will enjoy "brushing" through the doorway, and you'll be sure to see happy smiles as they do!

Visiting The Dentist

Plan a field trip to a dentist's office this month. Or use pictures to familiarize your students with the dental office setting and the procedures followed during a dental visit. Discuss with students why it is important to visit a dentist regularly. Have the children who have been to a dentist describe the equipment, dental instruments, members of the dental team, and role of each team member.

Demonstration Of Decay

Your students can observe the effect of decay with this simple demonstration. Obtain an unbruised apple. Make a hole in it, one inch deep. Set it aside for several days, protected from view in a paper bag. Cut through the place where the hole was made and have the class observe the effect of decay. Explain that this illustrates the way decay spreads through a tooth.

Snaggletooth Club

When a baby tooth comes out, it's a joyous time for little ones. Celebrate the event and keep up with the tooth by placing it in a Snaggletooth membership envelope. Duplicate the pattern on page 10 on construction paper. Cut out, fold, and glue the sides. Be prepared by keeping a stack of envelopes on hand. When a tooth comes out, pop it into an envelope, seal it with glue, and send it home.

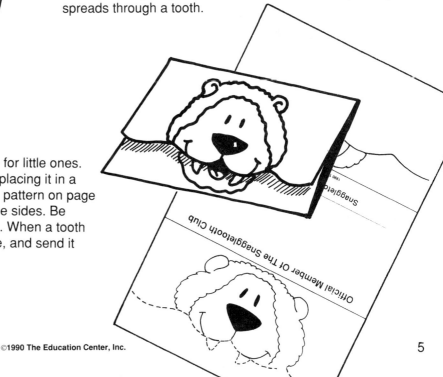

Teeth Are Important

Use these ideas to point out that teeth are necessary for chewing and speaking:
• On the board, list your students' favorite foods for meals and snacks. Discuss which of these foods can or cannot be eaten without teeth. Ask students to name foods that cannot be eaten by babies and explain.
• Pass out carrot sticks. Ask each child to cover his teeth with his lips while trying to bite into the carrot. Have students describe how their eating habits would change if they had no teeth.
• Write the following list of words on the board. Try saying them together. Have a student volunteer circle the words that have sounds made by your tongue touching your teeth. Have students name other words that cannot be said properly without using their teeth.

sun	pen	tap	can	led	him
big	rib	get	fudge	meet	kite
zero	jam	dim	doll	lick	will

The Bad News About Plaque

If your students watch television, then they've heard of *plaque*—but do they know what it is? Plaque is a sticky film that consists of saliva, food particles, and bacteria. The digestive action of the bacteria, when combined with sugar, forms an enamel-dissolving acid—not great news for healthy teeth! The only way to remove plaque is by brushing and flossing.

Make students aware of the risks of eating too many foods that are packed with sugar. For one day, have each child list everything he or she eats, including snacks. Have students work together in pairs or small groups to separate foods on their lists into sugar and no-sugar groups. As an extension, have students bring in empty food packages and examine them to find out which products contain sugar. (Don't forget other forms of sugar such as dextrose, maltose, sucrose, corn syrup, honey, etc.)

Why Should I Floss?

Even the best brushing technique won't completely eliminate damaging plaque. Teeth have six sides, creating some hard-to-reach places that your toothbrush often misses. Flossing helps clean these areas between the teeth and near your gum line.

To show the importance of flossing, have a volunteer brush his teeth thoroughly. Give him a disclosing tablet (available from a dentist) to chew. The tablet's vegetable dye will stain any plaque in the student's mouth. Have the student try to remove the stained plaque by chewing a stick of celery, rinsing his mouth with water, and chewing sugarless gum. Did any of these methods work? Have the student brush his teeth again. Did the brushing help? Finally, give the student another tablet to see if all the plaque is gone. Did the toothbrush still leave plaque between the teeth and near the gum line?

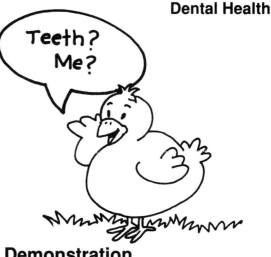

Toothy Talk

Share a chuckle during Dental Health Month by asking students these humorous questions:
- What's it like to bite off more than you can chew?
- What is something that is as scarce as hens' teeth?
- What do you do when you bite the bullet?
- What can be done about a sweet tooth?
- What do you do when you give someone the brush-off?

Plaque Demonstration

Sticky plaque holds acid from food to the surface of the tooth. The acid causes decay by making holes in the tooth's enamel covering. To demonstrate the effect of acid on teeth, soak an uncooked egg in vinegar for six hours. As acid eats through the shell, have students observe what happens to the inside of the egg. Is the eggshell still able to protect the egg inside? Point out that what acid does to the eggshell, it can do to teeth!

First Aid For Teeth

Be sure students are aware of steps to take if a permanent tooth is knocked out or loosened. If the tooth feels loose, a dentist should X-ray it for hidden breakage. If the tooth comes out, it should be placed immediately in a jar of liquid, preferably salt water or milk. If that's not possible, wrap the tooth in a wet paper towel. The idea is to keep the tooth from drying out. Gauze may be placed in the child's mouth to stop bleeding. Go to the dentist as soon as possible. You may wish to have students copy these steps on an index card to tape inside a medicine cabinet for future reference.

Brushing Melody

Teach children the following song to the tune of "Row, Row, Row Your Boat." Have them practice the toothbrushing motions holding their toothbrushes (or imaginary ones) out in front of them while they are singing.

Brush, brush, brush your teeth, brush them every day.
Right, left, up, down, clean the plaque away.
Brush, brush, brush your teeth, brush them every day.
Front, back, take off the plaque, now we smile all day.

Dental Health

With this motivational bulletin board, encourage students to brush their teeth regularly. Enlarge the pattern below to make the central figure. Duplicate and label the pattern for each student. Add a self-adhesive star to each student's cutout for each day that he brushes his teeth.

Pattern

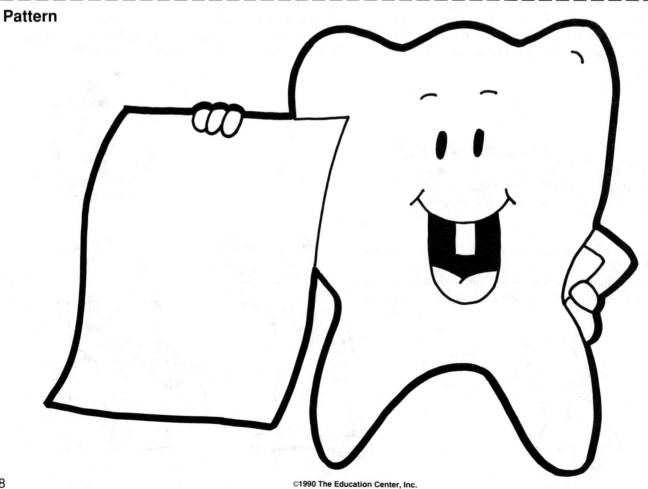

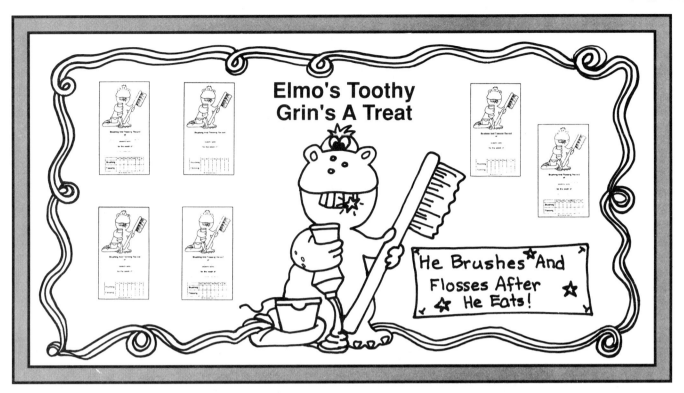

Smile! Elmo wants your students to have great dental hygiene. Enlarge Elmo from the brushing and flossing record below. Color, laminate, and mount on the board. For a border of "toothpaste," pin a length of heavy yarn or cord to the board. Duplicate the brushing and flossing record for each student. After recording their dental hygiene habits for one week, display these records along with Elmo.

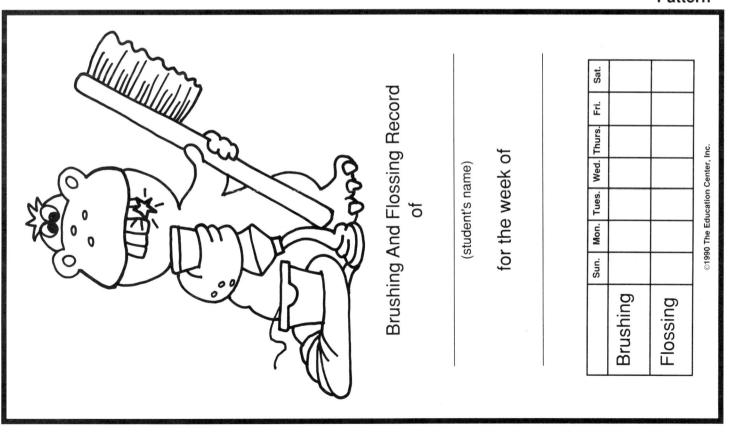

National Children's Dental Health Month
The
"Say Cheese" Award
goes to

_____
(student)

I like your
Picture-Perfect
Smile!

_____   _____
(date)   ©1990 The Education Center, Inc.   (teacher)

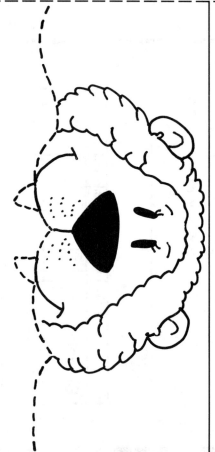

Official Member Of The Snaggletooth Club

Snaggletooth Club Member

©1990 The Education Center, Inc.

Note To Teacher: Give the award when a child loses a tooth, completes a dental health assignment, or has had a school dental health checkup. Use the Snaggletooth Award with the activity on page 5.

Name _____

Dental Health Is Important—NO "LION"!

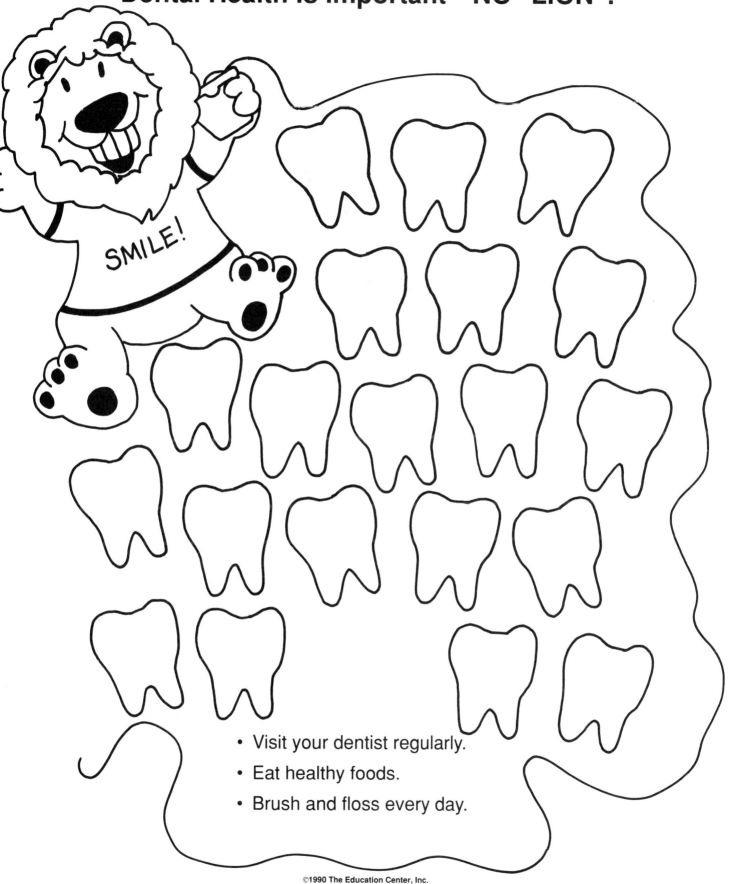

- Visit your dentist regularly.
- Eat healthy foods.
- Brush and floss every day.

©1990 The Education Center, Inc.

Note To Teacher: Program the teeth with math problems, words to divide into syllables, or another appropriate skill. Write directions at the top of the sheet.

Try This Snack!

Color Tommy Tooth's spaces **red**.

Color Mr. Plaque's spaces **black**.

Tommy will show you a healthy snack!

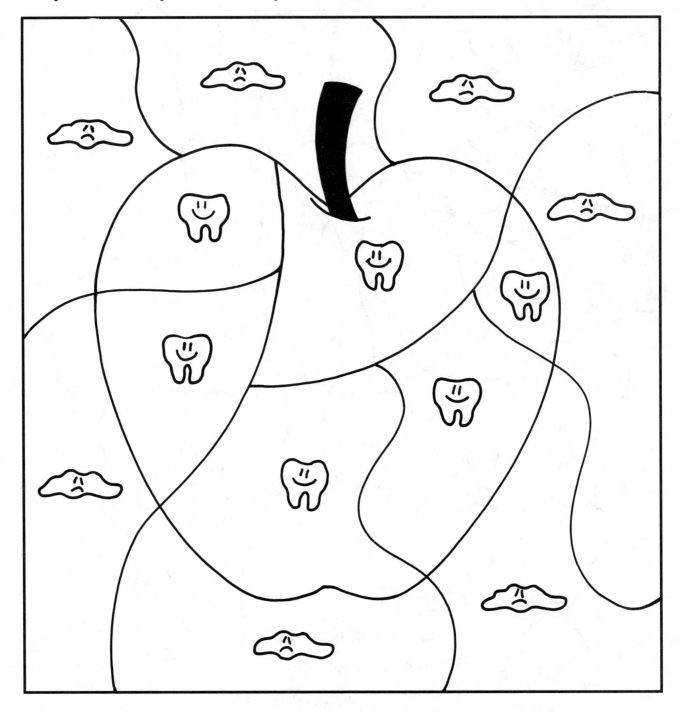

| **Bonus Box:** Draw your favorite healthy snack on the back. |

Name _____

Take Care Of Your Teeth!

1. Find and cut out the rules for healthy teeth.
2. Punch a hole in these tooth shapes.
3. String them on yarn.
4. Wear your necklace!

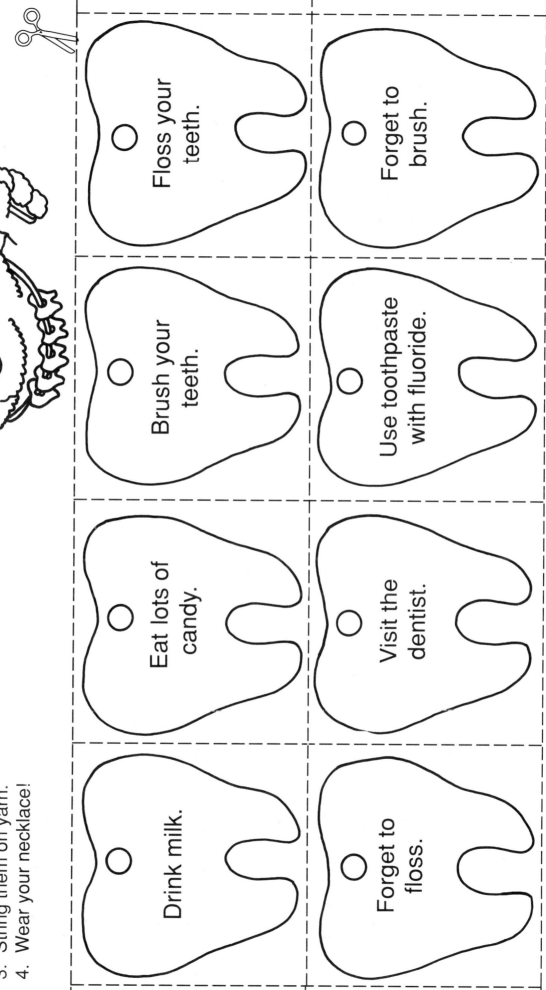

Floss your teeth.

Forget to brush.

Brush your teeth.

Use toothpaste with fluoride.

Eat lots of candy.

Visit the dentist.

Drink milk.

Forget to floss.

Note To Teacher: Provide students with scissors, yarn, and a hole punch.

Name _____

The Great Tooth Test

Write **T** for true or **F** for false in each blank.

_____ 1. Fruit does not have enough sugar to hurt your teeth.

_____ 2. Tooth decay can be hazardous to your health.

_____ 3. You should replace your toothbrush only when the bristles fall out.

_____ 4. Flossing daily is good for your teeth.

_____ 5. You shouldn't worry about a small hole in your tooth.

_____ 6. Every person grows two sets of teeth.

_____ 7. Molars are for grinding food.

_____ 8. If you can't brush after a meal, you should at least rinse with water.

_____ 9. Once tooth decay starts, only a dentist can stop it.

_____ 10. Incisors are for tearing food.

_____ 11. You should hold a toothbrush with two hands.

_____ 12. The root holds a tooth in place in the gums.

_____ 13. Your permanent teeth are your second set.

_____ 14. If you brush your teeth carefully, you don't need to floss.

_____ 15. You'll have fewer acid attacks on your teeth if you eat sweets only at mealtime.

_____ 16. A good way to remove plaque is to eat a piece of celery.

Now add the numbers of the statements marked **T.** If your total is 86, you're on the track to terrific teeth!

Bonus Box: Make a picture book for primary students that shows how to take care of teeth.

Warm Weather Or Cold, Mr. Groundhog?

Celebrate Groundhog Day on February 2 with these easy-to-make activities and useful reproducibles.

Mr. Groundhog's Shadow

Invite Mr. Groundhog into your classroom to give students a clever drill on opposites. Duplicate the pattern on page 16 on black and light brown construction paper. Label the cutouts with antonyms. (Use white peel-off labels for the black cutouts.) After matching each groundhog to its correct "shadow," have the student complete the worksheet on page 17 for additional practice. Make more groundhogs for matching math facts and answers, beginning sounds and pictures, upper- and lower-case letters, and other skills.

A Groundhog Display

Decorate a school hallway or long wall with the story of Groundhog Day. Duplicate the groundhog pattern on page 16 for each student on grey construction paper. Have each child cut out his groundhog; then have him cut out a hole from black construction paper and place his groundhog in the hole. Mount the groundhogs on the wall with "bubble" captions that tell the story.

Groundhog Pocket Pal

When they poke their heads from this Pocket Pal, the groundhogs predict practice in sequencing. Use the pattern on page 16 to make eight cut-out groundhogs. Label each with a word. Program the backs so that the cutouts spell "FORECAST" when turned over. Place the cutouts in a manila envelope and write student directions on the front as shown.

Vary this activity for alphabetical order of letters, sentence order, or ordering numbers or fractions.

Groundhog Day Pattern

Use with the
activities on
page 15.

Name _____

Wake Up, Mr. Groundhog!

Write the opposite of each word in the blank.
Use the words on the ground.

1. never _____

2. near _____

3. lost _____

4. hard _____

5. high _____

6. fat _____

7. frown _____

8. best _____

9. buy _____

10. clean _____

11. sour _____

12. dry _____

13. huge _____

14. noisy _____

15. happy _____

Color the picture of Mr. Groundhog when you are finished!

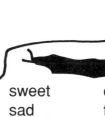

sweet	quiet	soft
sad	thin	dirty
always	low	worst
far	sell	found
smile	tiny	wet

Sunny Or Cloudy?

Note To Teacher: Program the clouds and suns with math problems, missing-blend words, words to abbreviate, or any other skill.
Add directions at the top of the sheet.

Name _____

It's Groundhog Day!

1. Read the sentences.
2. Number them in order.
3. Then cut them apart and paste them in order on another sheet of paper.
4. Draw a picture to go with your story.

_____ If the groundhog does not see his shadow and stays outside, warm weather is coming.

_____ People gather to watch the groundhog on February second.

_____ Then he looks for his shadow.

_____ The groundhog comes out of his hole.

_____ But if he sees his shadow, the groundhog will run back into his hole.

_____ This means we will have six more weeks of cold weather.

Note To Teacher: Provide each child with scissors, glue, and a piece of construction paper.

You Gotta Have Heart!

Usher in this special season of love, hearts, and sweet sentiments with lots of special Valentine's Day activities and reproducibles.

Conversation Hearts

A few days before Valentine's Day, give each of your students six to eight candy conversation hearts. Have each child write a story using the words on his or her hearts; then let the students eat their candies. On Valentine's Day, hold a sharing session during which each student reads his story to the class.

Healthy Hearts

Introduce students to the importance of healthy hearts during February, which is American Heart Month. Ask a representative from a local fitness center or YWCA/YMCA to demonstrate aerobic exercise and explain its importance. Invite a school or hospital dietician to speak to the class about good nutrition for healthy hearts. Resolve to institute one healthy habit each week in your class, such as an aerobic game or daily class walk.

Candy Counting

You can count on this easy center to give preschool and kindergarten children lots of counting practice. Line a muffin tin with 12 paper liners. Label the paper liners with numbers from one to 12. Place a bowl or Ziploc bag of candy hearts nearby. Each child counts out the correct number of hearts into each cup. Change the liners for practice with number words.

Pipe Cleaner Hearts

Give your students an inexpensive and unusual valentine treat. Purchase one red pipe cleaner for each of your students. Shape one end of each pipe cleaner into a heart shape. Wrap the other end around a pencil.

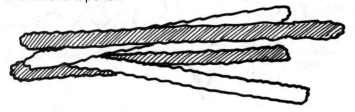

Have A Heart

Use a valentine theme to help build self-esteem among your students. Duplicate a paper heart that has lines numbered from one to ten. (See the heart pattern on page 27.) Pin one heart to each student's back. Classmates move about the room and write one good thing about each student without signing their names. This continues until all ten lines on each heart have been filled. Remove the hearts and give the children time to read the positive comments that were written.

Sweetheart Lunch

Surprise your students by inviting them to join you for lunch during the week of Valentine's Day. Cover a large table with a red-and-white tablecloth and provide chairs for one-fifth of your class. Each day invite a new group of sweethearts to eat their lunches around the table with you. Add to the festivities by providing holiday napkins and dinner music.

Valentine Message Math

Get more mileage out of boxed valentines by printing math problems on the reverse side. Laminate the cards and have students complete problems with a grease pencil.

Making Hearts

Young students often have difficulty making hearts. Use this poem to help them:

First you make a <u>V</u>.
Then turn your paper and make a <u>three</u>.
Cut me out, and…
A valentine heart you'll see!

Heart Full Of Good Deeds

Challenge your students to fill a king-size heart with kindness and good deeds during the month of February. Draw a large heart on a sheet of white poster board. Inside the heart draw various sizes of small hearts. Have a student color in one small heart each time he is observed displaying kindness or performing a good deed. If all of the small hearts are colored by the end of the month, your students will have met your challenge!

Valentine Surprises

Expect tons of hugs when you give your students these valentines. Duplicate hearts onto red and pink construction paper. (See the small heart pattern on page 27.) Address one heart for each student in your classroom; then cut out and weave a new, sharpened pencil through each heart.

Dear Sara,
You may turn this valentine in for an assignment of your choice.
Love,
Mrs. Hall

You SUIT me just fine! Be mine!

Colorful Valentine Cards

Provide students with magazines, department store ads, and nursery catalogs to create and decorate their own valentines. To get them started, you may suggest using a clothing ad with the saying, "You SUIT me just fine! Be mine!" or an ad for a watch to illustrate, "It's TIME to be my valentine!" Use the nursery catalogs to create romantic cards with floral collages.

Lonely Hearts Club

During this month of love and friendship, inaugurate a lonely hearts club. Contact a local nursing or retirement home for the names of residents who would like to exchange correspondence with your class. Students may make cards, pictures, or crafts to send to their pen pals. Watch love grow when responses arrive from the senior citizens.

Valentine Collage

What do you do with all the valentines that students give you? Demonstrate to the class that you are proud of each and every card. Staple valentines in collage form on a bulletin board. Add the words "I Love You Too."

A Valentine For The Principal

A few weeks before Valentine's Day, as a daily reward for good behavior, allow students to decorate a big heart for their principal. Each student should get a chance to add his or her personal touch. Paper lace can be added to finish the heart. To complete the surprise, actually mail the valentine instead of delivering it. Your principal will love it!

HAPPY VALENTINE'S DAY!

Valentine's Day Party Page

Everyone will feel loved when you incorporate these festive ideas into your Valentine's Day party.

Postman, Postman

Everyone gets to participate in this game involving a hidden valentine. Choose one child to be the postman and give him or her the postman's hat. (See illustration.) The postman must hide his eyes while you give another child a valentine to hide. Then the postman uncovers his eyes and faces his classmates who say, "Postman, Postman, where's the mail?" The postman gets three guesses to find out who is hiding the mail. If he guesses correctly, he continues as postman. If he is unsuccessful, the person with the mail becomes the postman.

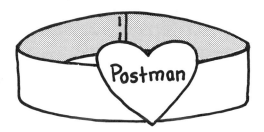

Cupcake Stencils

Have children help bake cupcakes in pink paper liners and prepare white frosting. Make paper stencils in heart and dove shapes (see patterns). Let each child place a stencil on his frosted cupcake and sprinkle with red sugar crystals. Carefully remove the stencil to reveal a valentine!

Patterns

Valentine Necklaces

Bake these valentines several days ahead so everyone will have a heart to wear at the party. Mix 1 cup salt, 3 cups flour, and 1/2 cup warm water. Add a few drops of red food coloring. Knead until smooth. Roll as you would cookie dough. Let children use cookie cutters to cut out heart shapes. Poke a straw into each cutout before baking to make a hole for hanging. Bake at 250 degrees for about 30 minutes or until hard. Have children paint hearts and spray with acrylic spray. When dry, have each child thread a piece of yarn through his heart and tie it around his neck. Heart necklaces may be given to parents or special friends after the party.

1. 9" cake pans

2. Cut the round layer in half.

3. Assemble.

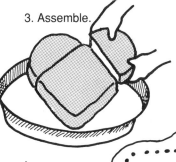

Valentine Cake

You can make a special Valentine's Day cake by using one square and one round cake pan. Prepare a cake mix as directed and bake in the two shaped pans. When cool, cut the round layer, as shown, and assemble with the square layer to make a heart shape. Frost with white icing and trim with candy red-hots.

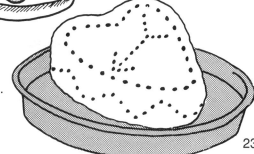

Cut an identical red and white heart pair for each student. Attach the white heart cutout to a good work sample belonging to each student and mount on a bulletin board. Enlarge the cupid pattern on page 26. Color, laminate, and mount it on the board. Have each student cut his red heart cutout into four pieces and then store the pieces in a small envelope labeled with his name. During the month of February, reward each student for exemplary behavior or work by attaching a piece of his red heart cutout atop his white heart. Be sure to point out at least four positive traits for each student by the end of February so that each child will have a completed red heart to take home.

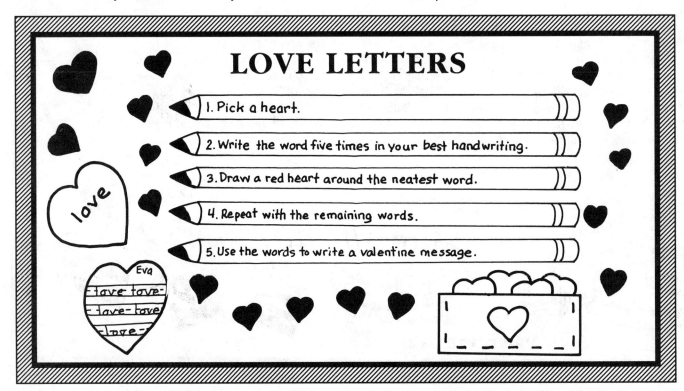

To make this handwriting board, label cut-out hearts with words (see the heart patterns on page 27). Place the hearts in a large pocket attached to the board. Cut handwriting paper into heart shapes and place in the pocket. For fun, give valentine pencils as rewards for improved handwriting.

This lacy valentine door decoration radiates love and kindness. On white construction paper or tagboard, duplicate the cupid and heart patterns on page 26. Color patterns; then cut on the dotted lines with an X-acto knife before cutting them out. Attach a student's photograph (or a photocopy of a school photo) to the back of each cutout; then mount on the giant heart cutout. Lace can be added by carefully ruffling, then taping, four-inch tissue paper strips to the back of the heart cutout. Punch holes along the outside border of the "lace" for an eyelet effect.

Students will enjoy creating their own hearts for this colorful bulletin board. Provide a heart cutout for each student (see pattern on page 27). Have each student dribble white glue randomly on his cutout. Allow to dry overnight. Then have each student paint over the dried glue with red and blue watercolor paints.

Valentine's Day Patterns

Use the cupid pattern with "Fabulous February Hearts" on page 24.

Use with door display on page 25.

Use with door display on page 25.

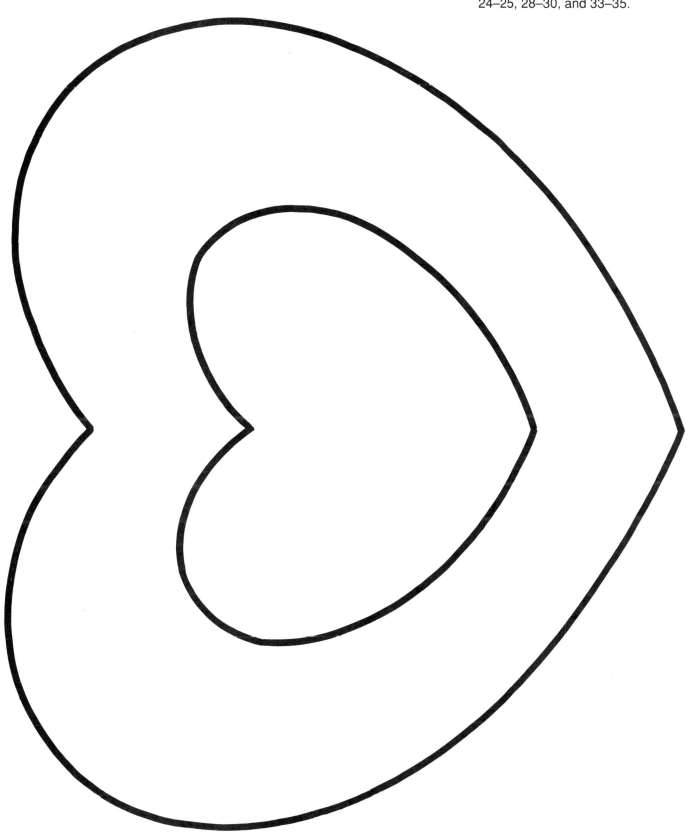

27

Valentine's Day Centers

Love Those Love Letters

Now that everyone is checking their mailboxes for valentines, it's the perfect time to provide practice in addressing envelopes. Label index cards with incorrectly written addresses as shown. Place at a center with a real mailbox or shoebox labeled "MAIL." A student chooses an index card, rewrites the address correctly on his paper or on an actual envelope, and deposits his work in the mailbox. Correctly addressed letters earn students bonus points good for extra library time, a "No Homework" pass, or another treat. To add more practice, have each child write his address incorrectly on an index card and add it to the stack.

miss heartfelt joy
somewhere special alabama
2438 lover's lane

miss fancy whitelace
22 rosebud court
loveland colorado

miss teen angel
1000 heavenly way
saint cloud minnesota

mr and mrs lovely people
2515 sweetheart rd
love and kisses florida

mr cupid dart
straight arrow north dakota
10 bow st

Heart-To-Heart

Tongue depressors make this Valentine's Day center extra special. Glue one large and four small construction paper hearts inside a file folder. (See heart patterns on page 27.) Laminate the folder; then slit open the top of each heart to make a pocket. With a wipe-off marker, program the small pockets with numbers. Write matching math facts on small paper hearts glued to tongue depressors. The student places each heart-on-a-stick in the correct pocket. Vary this idea by programming the pockets and hearts with rhyming words, beginning consonants/pictures, and clock faces/times.

A Perfect Match

A package of assorted valentines or a collection of valentines from past years is all you need to make this visual discrimination center. Choose several identical pairs of valentines; then attach one valentine from each pair to the inside of a file folder. Laminate the folder for durability if desired. Students lay each remaining valentine atop its perfect match.

To Have A Friend, Be One

Focus on friendship during the Valentine's Day season with this critical thinking center. Label paper heart cutouts with the words listed below (see heart pattern on page 27). Place the hearts in a paper bag decorated on the front and back as shown. The student reads the words in the bag and decides which words describe a friend. He then uses the words in five or more sentences about friends. Let your students add their own adjectives to the bag as well.

kind	cooperative	lying	loyal
honest	grouchy	dishonest	unpleasant
considerate	stingy	pleasant	trusting
truthful	generous	unfriendly	unhappy
loving	hot-tempered	greedy	friendly
unkind	selfish	cruel	angry
hateful	cheerful	thoughtful	gossiping
		happy	sharing

Mail Call

Use inexpensive valentines to make grammar practice a treat. Attach three construction paper mailbags to the inside of the folder for pockets. Circle one word on each of 20 valentines. Students look at the circled word on each valentine and place it in the correct pocket.

Valentine Mail

All you need to sweeten money skills is a package of commercial valentines. Using money stamps, stamp a coin amount on the back of each valentine. "Address" the envelopes with matching amounts. The student inserts each valentine inside its matching envelope. For self-checking, "hide" the correct amount somewhere on the front of each valentine. Store the valentines and envelopes in a valentine candy box or canister.

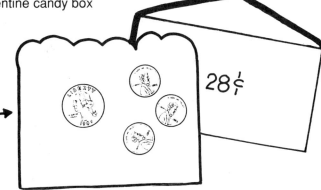

29

Art Activities Straight From The Heart

Heartstring Art

Give "heartstrings" a tug to create these lacy valentine projects. Pour pink and white tempera paint into pie tins. Clip a clothespin onto each of two 12-inch pieces of string. Holding one clothespin, dip the string in pink paint and drag the paint-laden string across a piece of red construction paper. Repeat this process using the other string and the white paint. When the string painting is dry, trace a heart outline (pattern on page 27) onto the paper and cut out. Cut paper doilies into eighths. Glue these doily sections onto the back of the heart cutout to create a lacy border.

Salt Dough Photo Frames

Salt dough photo frames are neat holiday gifts for students to make for their parents. Mix two parts flour with one part salt. Add a little water slowly to achieve the same texture as Play-Doh. Give each child enough dough to roll into a fat snake. Turn the snake into a heart by joining its ends. Smooth the ends together and insert a paper clip in the heart to use for hanging. Let the frames dry for several days, or bake them in an oven at 250 degrees for one hour. When the frames are completely dry, they can be painted or shellacked. Attach a small photograph to the back of the frame.

Hearts And Flowers

This simple valentine gift is created using a nine-inch square of red construction paper, a 3" X 9" piece of pink construction paper, assorted construction paper scraps, scissors, and glue. Begin by folding the red square and cutting it into the shape of a heart. Then lay the bottom of the heart on the pink rectangle, trace that portion of the heart, and cut on the lines. Glue the edges of the pink piece to the bottom of the heart to make a pocket. Create flowers using construction paper and tuck them into the heart. Add Valentine's Day greetings to the front of the heart.

Heart Prints

For a fun February activity, give each child a ball of modeling clay to mold into a heart shape. Have children dip their hearts into red, pink, or purple paint. Let students make prints on art paper or newsprint, or on a large piece of white paper tacked to your classroom door. When the hearts dry, have each student use a black marker to sign his heart

"Elephantastic" Valentine Bag

This pretty pachyderm is only hungry for valentines! Be sure to demonstrate each step for your students.

Materials:
brown paper bag
gray or brown construction paper
pencil
glue
scissors
red or white heart doily
two red, one-inch hearts
black crayon

Directions:
1. Fold construction paper into thirds.
2. Cut about halfway up on the fold lines.
3. Draw the ears on the two outside sections.
4. Glue two small hearts for eyes. Add brows.
5. Draw the trunk. Cut the elephant out.
6. Roll the trunk around a pencil.
7. Glue the heart doily above the eyes.
8. Glue the elephant to a brown bag. Use it to hold valentines.

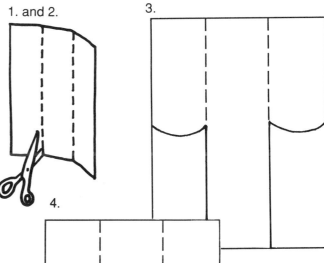

1. and 2.

3.

4.

5.

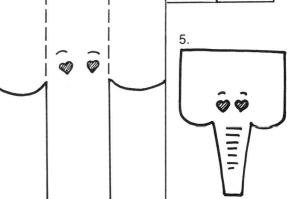

Valentine Heart Sculpture

Your students will delight in this opportunity to be creative. Provide various colors of construction paper, scissors, and glue. Students cut out several hearts of differing colors and sizes. By folding, slitting, and gluing, they create original, three-dimensional sculptures.

Hanging Heart Mobiles

Decorate your room with dainty valentine mobiles!

Materials:

three large red hearts	three smaller pink hearts
glue	scissors
yarn	white lace or paper doilies, cut for trimming

Steps:

1. Fold the red hearts in half; then open and lay them flat on the table.
2. Dab a little glue on the left side of one red heart. (Avoid gluing near the edges.)
3. Place a second red heart atop this heart, and press left sides together. The left side is now doubled in thickness.
4. Fold over the right side of the heart to the left and dab glue as before.
5. Place one end of the yarn in the center as shown and glue on the last red heart.
6. Glue the right side of the top heart to the remaining heart half.
7. Fold the three pink hearts in half; then glue each in the center of a red heart.
8. Glue white trim between the edges of the red hearts.
9. Hang your finished mobile to swing in the breeze!

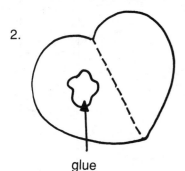

2.

glue

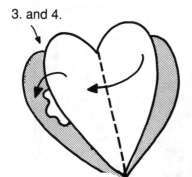

3. and 4.

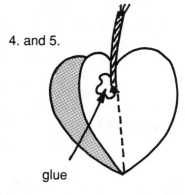

4. and 5.

glue

Valentine Necklace

Let your students know you care with this personalized necklace. Cut several plastic straws into one-inch pieces. Cut out small, red construction paper hearts. Punch a hole in each heart; then label with the name of a student. Alternate stringing the straw pieces and the hearts on a length of yarn or string. Tie the yarn in a knot when stringing is completed. Students can also make these necklaces for special loved ones on Valentine's Day.

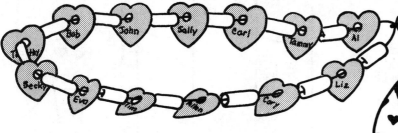

A Big Broken Heart

Enlist your students to help you mend a broken heart. Cut out a large heart from white butcher paper. Then cut the heart into puzzle pieces, one for each student in your class. Number the backs of the pieces for easy reconstruction. Have each student use chalk, crayons, markers, or paint (in shades of red and pink *only*) to design his puzzle piece. When everyone is finished, tape the puzzle back together and display on a bulletin board or wall. Use this idea for any holiday shape: shamrock, Easter egg, Christmas tree, pumpkin.

32

fold

Stand-up Valentine Bird

Here's a nice valentine project that doubles as a colorful classroom decoration and a gift for parents. Each student will need:

    one 3" X 5" index card
    one 4" red construction paper square
    one 3" pink construction paper square
    one 2" pink construction paper square
    pink and red construction paper strips
    glue
    scissors
    markers

Fold the index card as shown. Then cut a heart from each of the squares. Glue the hearts and strips together as shown. Using markers, add a beak and a heart-shaped eye. Glue the bird to the index-card base.

Hearts Worth Framing

Here is a quiet art activity that children will love! Provide each student with a tagboard heart pattern (see page 27), two sheets of 9" X 12" construction paper (one red or pink, one white), a red and/or pink marker, glue, and scissors. Instruct the student to fill the white paper with heart designs by randomly tracing the pattern with the red marker. Next have the student decorate each heart with a different design. To make a frame, have the child fold the red construction paper in half and cut as shown. The student then glues the heart design behind the red frame and trims the edges.

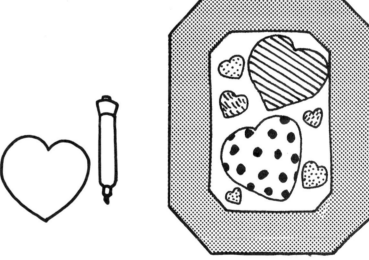

Cupid's Crinkled Creations

Looking for an unusual valentine project? Crinkled, aluminum foil hearts will fit the bill. Have each student crinkle and flatten a piece of aluminum foil before cutting it into the shape of a heart (patterns on page 27). With a mixture of egg yolk, powdered detergent, and red food coloring, have each student paint his heart cutout, leaving a bit of foil showing here and there. Allow for drying time. Have students glue the foil hearts onto red construction paper and trim to within 1/2 inch of the edge of the foil.

Animated Valentines

Do something different with hearts this Valentine's Day! After cutting out hearts of various sizes, glue them to white paper to form favorite animals, adding details with crayons or markers. A great imagination stretcher!

Valentines For Stuffing

Delight your youngsters with these folded paper valentine holders. To make, fold a 12" X 18" piece of red construction paper in half (Step 1). Then fold the lower corners up to the center line as shown (Step 2). Fold the front upper flap downward (Step 3), fold the protruding corners to the back, and staple in place (Step 4). Trim the upper corners to create a heart shape (Step 5). Have students embellish their valentine holders with stickers, heart-shaped cutouts, glitter, and assorted craft items. Then let students start stuffing their valentine holders with sentimental greetings.

1.

2.

3.

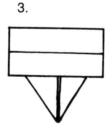

4.

Fold back.

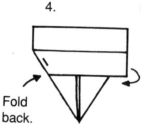

5. Cut shape.

Hearts In Bloom

Plant a garden of valentine messages in just one afternoon! Have each child cut out three construction paper hearts of the same size (patterns on page 27) and a green stem with leaves. Attach the hearts to the top of the stem with a brad. Use a fine-tipped marker to add a special message to take home to a loved one.

34

©1990 The Education Center, Inc.

Let's Play A Valentine's Day Game!

Valentine Bingo

Here's a game your students make themselves! Using a pencil and a ruler, each child draws a bingo card (five squares across and down). With your students, brainstorm a list of Valentine's Day words. List the words on the chalkboard as children call them out. Students complete their cards by writing a word in each square. To play, students cover words that are called out until someone covers five words across, down, or diagonally. For fun, use candy conversation hearts as markers; then eat the tasty treats when the game is over!

VALENTINE				
B	I	N	G	O
smile	white	hug	pink	flowers
love	cute	lace	sweets	pal
kiss	heart	♥	card	candy
party	friend	games	kind	caring
treats	fun	red	Cupid	arrow

VALENTINE				
B	I	N	G	O
pink	red	lace	pal	heart
candy	card	friend	Cupid	arrow
fun	kiss	♥	hug	love
sweets	love	wish	party	smile
flowers	games	happy	caring	cute

Number Facts Valentine Game

Heart necklaces hang around for this fun math game. Label a supply of paper hearts with math facts and their matching answers. Punch two holes in each heart and string with yarn. Choose one child to be IT. Give each of the other children a math fact heart to wear.

To play, have the children sit in a circle. Place an answer heart around IT's neck without the child seeing it. IT goes around the circle from player to player asking, "Will you be my valentine?" If the player is wearing a math fact that matches IT's answer heart, he says, "Yes," and IT responds, "Then my answer must be _____." If correct, the children exchange places, and the new IT receives a new answer heart to wear. If incorrect, the student continues around the circle until he finds another matching fact.

Heart Hunt

Mend a class full of broken hearts on Valentine's Day! Make enough paper hearts for half of your class (see the patterns on page 27). Cut them in two and give each student a half. At your signal, each student finds the person who has the other half of his heart. When everyone has found his match, the partners tape and decorate the "mended" heart together. Attach the hearts to a February bulletin board or wall mural.

February

Kindness Calendar

Number the days in February.

Draw a smiley heart on each day that you do something to show love or kindness to someone.

Sunday	Monday	Tuesday	Wednesday	Thursday	Friday	Saturday

Earn A Valentine Surprise By Reading!

Read _____ minutes at home each day. Ask your parent to sign on the lines below.

Color in a section of the heart daily.

1. _____
2. _____
3. _____
4. _____
5. _____

Give this to your teacher when you are done and earn a valentine surprise!

Note To Teacher: Fill in the appropriate number of minutes. Duplicate on white construction paper. Send home weekly with students. Award each student who returns a completed form with a prize such as a valentine pencil, eraser, or sugarless treat.

Be My Valentine

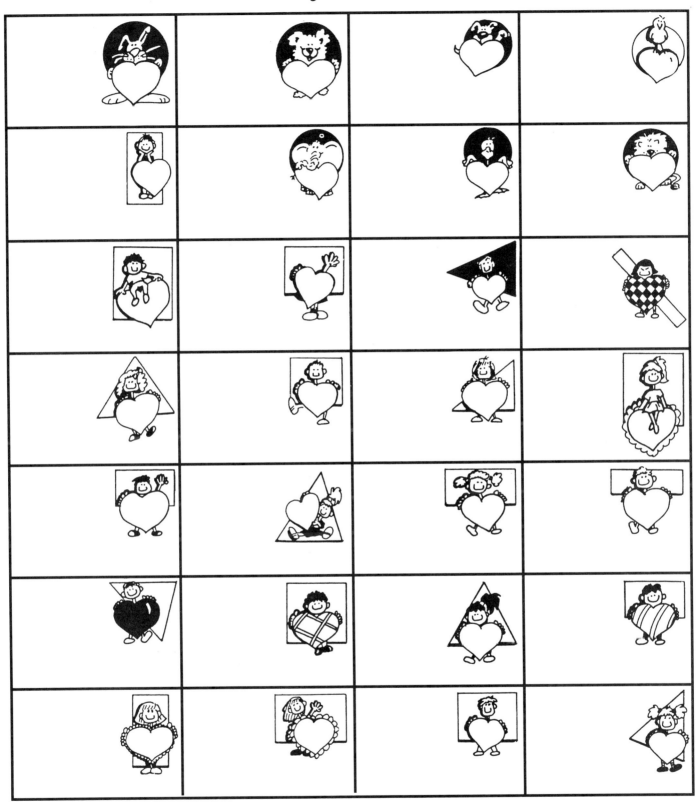

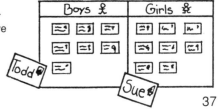

You Set My Heart On Fire!

Keep up
the red-hot work!

Note To Teacher: Program the hearts with math problems, scrambled spelling words, word pairs to write as contractions, or any appropriate skill. Write a list of words on the board for students to alphabetize on the sheet.

Note To Teacher: Program with a Valentine's Day message, February class newsletter, math problems, or review questions. Add lines and use for creative writing or handwriting assignments.

Rhyming words

Mailbox Valentines

Write the rhyming words on the correct mailboxes.

blue

cat

head

meat

rain

bread

dew

said

feet

plane

treat

you

train

rat

flat

SUE
1.
2.
3.

FRED
1.
2.
3.

PETE
1.
2.
3.

JANE
1.
2.
3.

MATT
1.
2.
3.

Bonus Box: Use three of the words in a valentine poem. Draw a picture to go with your poem.

©1990 The Education Center, Inc. • Key pp. 126–128

Name _____

Write the missing
numbers.

Color the even
numbers red.

Candy Hearts

0 1 2

13

20   28

                              36

                  44

                          57

                                              69

            72

                                      88

      91

Love Is A Warm Feeling

Draw a heart around *only* problems with correct answers.

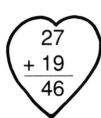
```
  27
+ 19
----
  46
```

```
  34
+ 26
----
  50
```

```
  25
+ 27
----
  52
```

```
  63
+ 28
----
  91
```

```
  42
+ 29
----
  71
```

```
  18
+ 38
----
  57
```

```
  56
+ 25
----
  91
```

```
  19
+ 44
----
  63
```

```
  32
+ 58
----
  90
```

```
  16
+ 19
----
  34
```

```
  27
+ 48
----
  75
```

```
  33
+ 49
----
  83
```

```
  25
+ 39
----
  64
```

```
  17
+ 54
----
  71
```

```
  29
+ 58
----
  76
```

```
  17
+ 57
----
  75
```

```
  35
+ 58
----
  93
```

```
  39
+ 19
----
  59
```

```
  26
+ 28
----
  54
```

```
  55
+ 26
----
  81
```

Bonus Box: Correct the incorrect answers.

Valentine Book Report Mobile

Directions:
1. Select and read a book.
2. Fill in each piece; then cut it out.
3. Glue each piece to red or pink construction paper. Cut around the piece, leaving a 1/4" border of construction paper.
4. Tape one end of a piece of yarn to the back of each piece.
5. Tie the pieces to a coat hanger to complete your mobile.

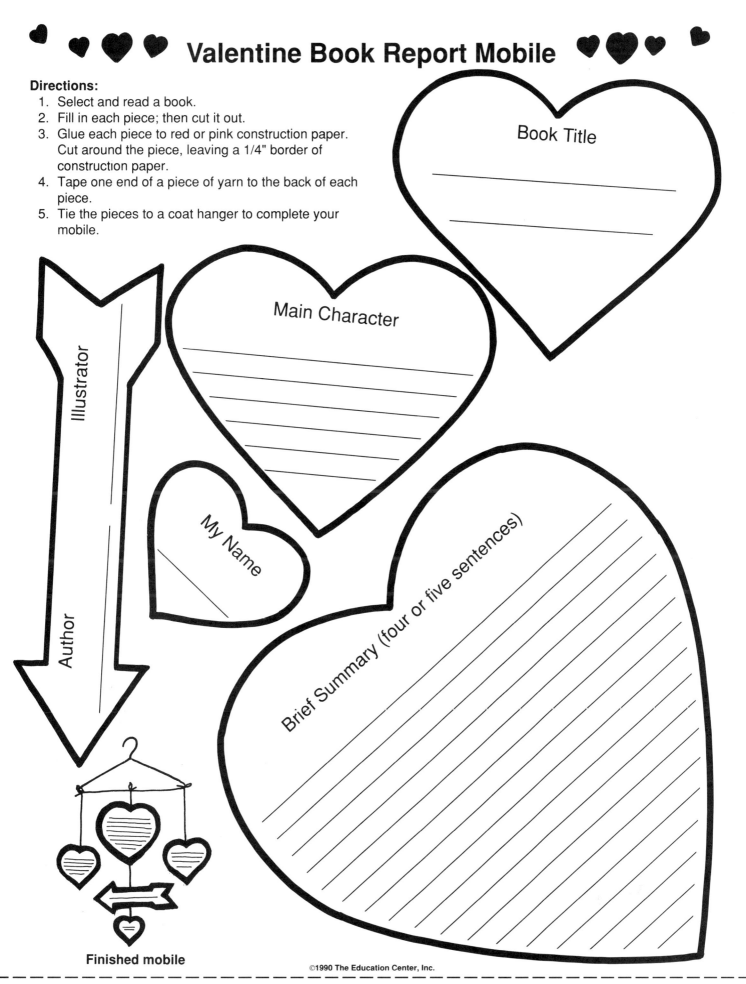

Book Title

Main Character

Illustrator

Author

My Name

Brief Summary (four or five sentences)

Finished mobile

©1990 The Education Center, Inc.

Note To Teacher: Provide each student with red and/or pink construction paper, scissors, glue, yarn, tape, and a coat hanger.

Name _____

Lovesick Serenade

Write the answer in each note.
Circle your answers in the number search.

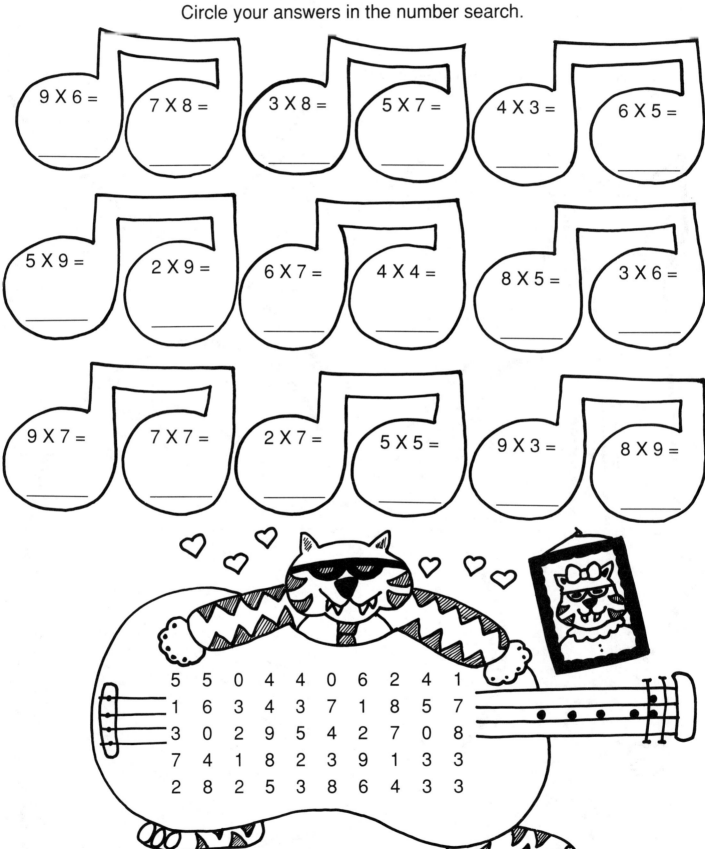

9 X 6 = ___ 7 X 8 = ___ 3 X 8 = ___ 5 X 7 = ___ 4 X 3 = ___ 6 X 5 = ___

5 X 9 = ___ 2 X 9 = ___ 6 X 7 = ___ 4 X 4 = ___ 8 X 5 = ___ 3 X 6 = ___

9 X 7 = ___ 7 X 7 = ___ 2 X 7 = ___ 5 X 5 = ___ 9 X 3 = ___ 8 X 9 = ___

```
5  5  0  4  4  0  6  2  4  1
1  6  3  4  3  7  1  8  5  7
3  0  2  9  5  4  2  7  0  8
7  4  1  8  2  3  9  1  3  3
2  8  2  5  3  8  6  4  3  3
```

Celebrating Black History

Look beyond the Jamestown slave ships to the arrival of our country's first explorers, and you'll find the beginning of black history in America. Enlighten your students to the richness of our African American heritage with these activities and the reproducibles on pages 49–52.

The ABCs of Black History

Spotlighting outstanding African Americans is as easy as A, B, C with this bulletin board activity. Have each student choose a famous African American to research (see the resource list on page 48). Provide patterns to help each child trace and cut out large poster board letters of his person's initials. Have students write descriptive words, phrases, and sentences about their famous African Americans on the letters. Display on a bulletin board entitled "The ABCs Of Black History."

Stamps Of Approval

On April 7, 1940, the Booker T. Washington stamp went on sale at Tuskegee Institute in Alabama. It was the first United States postage stamp to honor an African American. Since that time, other commemorative stamps have been issued to honor African Americans. These include poet Paul Laurence Dunbar, scientist George Washington Carver, composer W.C. Handy, and artist Henry Ossawa Tanner. Dr. Martin Luther King, Jr., is shown on more postage stamps from around the world than any other African American.

Challenge students to "strike" new commemorative stamps in honor of African Americans. Divide your class into committees. Have each committee choose an outstanding African American to research. Provide poster board and other art supplies for groups to design their stamps. Use pinking shears to trim the edges of each stamp for an authentic look. When the stamps are completed, have each committee share its stamp and reasons for honoring its African American.

PAUL LAURENCE DUNBAR

Sweet Dreams

For many years in our country, African Americans dreamed of an end to slavery. After a bloody, costly war, that dream was realized. Give your children time to ponder their dreams for America; then begin an American Dream Quilt. Pass out 12-inch squares of construction paper for the background blocks. Have students use fabric, wallpaper samples, or art paper to make appliqués representing their dreams. Glue completed blocks on a large piece of paper, leaving spaces between the blocks to achieve the quilted look. Hang your attractive dream quilt in the classroom, library, hallway, or cafeteria.

No More War!

Freedom's Flame

Make your students more aware of the tremendous contributions of African Americans with this matching center. Use the patterns on page 47 to make several tagboard torches and flames. Cover the torches with aluminum foil and use a permanent marker to label with the names of famous African Americans. Write matching achievements on the flames. (See the resource list on page 48.) Number code the backs of the pieces for easy self-checking.

The Peanut Man

George Washington Carver helped to change the economy of the South by making it less dependent on cotton production. His ideas were published by the Department of Agriculture for farmers all over the world. He donated his life savings to the George Washington Carver Foundation which continues his farm research.

Have the children write about George Washington Carver in a peanut-shaped booklet. Instruct children to trace two peanut shapes on manila paper and cut them out for covers. Have students illustrate these captions:

- As a boy, George Washington Carver was a slave and an orphan. He went to a school for black children when he was ten.
- George liked to study plants. He went to college to learn about agriculture.
- Mr. Carver became a teacher and scientist at Tuskegee Institute in Alabama. He found ways to make plants grow bigger and better.
- He invented many uses for the peanut, sweet potato, and soybean.
- His work has helped farmers all over the world.

Display booklets with products made from peanuts, sweet potatoes, and soybeans.

Oral Black History

Because most slaves could not read or write, they passed their history on by telling it to generation after generation. Have young children listen as you read about these famous African Americans. Then see how many names they can remember. To follow up, you may want to have each child illustrate an accomplishment by a famous African American.

- Marian Anderson sang in the White House.
- Ronald McNair was a crew member on the space shuttle, *Challenger*.
- Harriet Tubman helped slaves escape to freedom by guiding them to safe places called the Underground Railroad.
- Jesse Jackson was a candidate for president.
- Martin Luther King was a minister who worked for equal rights for all people.
- Matthew Henson was an explorer who reached the North Pole.
- Jesse Owens won gold medals in the Olympics.
- Mary McLeod Bethune started schools for black students.

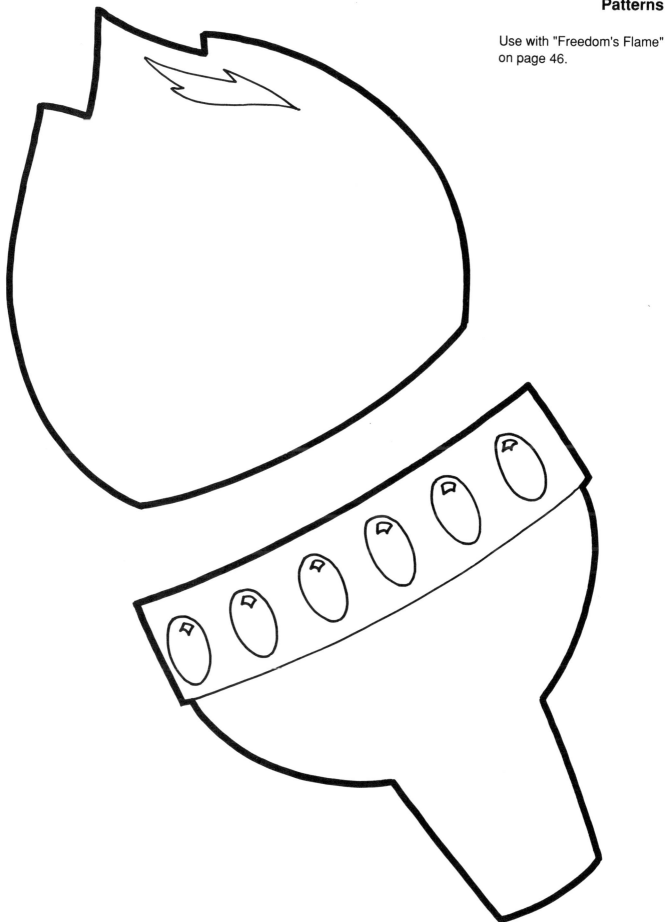

Salute Black History Month with this star-studded display. Have students cut out and mount magazine pictures to create a collage in observance of Black History Month. Program 28 star cutouts (pattern below) with the numbers one through 28. On the back of each cutout, write the name of a famous African American (see list below). Mount cutouts and a calendar grid as shown. Share a few facts about the African American listed on the back of each daily cutout.

Famous African Americans

Louis Armstrong—Famous jazz trumpeter
Bill Robinson—"Bojangles," dancer of 1920s and 1930s
Benjamin Banneker—Built one of first clocks in America
Harriet Tubman—Leader of the Underground Railroad
Crispus Attucks—Hero of the Boston Massacre
Robert C. Weaver—First African American Cabinet member
Shirley Chisholm—First African American woman in Congress
Daniel Hale Williams—Performed first successful heart operation
W.C. Handy—Blues writer
Booker T. Washington—Educator
Mary McLeod Bethune—Educator
Phillis Wheatley—Poet
Ronald McNair—Space shuttle astronaut
Charles Drew—Established first blood bank
Thurgood Marshall—First African American Supreme Court justice
Jackie Robinson—First African American to play major league baseball
Jesse Jackson—Civil rights leader, candidate for president
Frederick Douglass—Famous orator, spoke against slavery
William Still—Composer
Duke Ellington—Famous jazz composer, bandleader, pianist
Sojourner Truth—Traveled and spoke against slavery

Wilma Rudolph—Olympic runner
Jesse Owens—Gold medal winner in 1936 Olympics
Langston Hughes—Famous novelist and poet
Martin Luther King, Jr.—Led civil rights movement in 1960s
Matthew Henson—Reached North Pole with Robert E. Peary
Althea Gibson—One of world's greatest female tennis players
Nat Turner—Led slave revolt during Civil War
Marian Anderson—Famous singer
George Washington Carver—Inventor and scientist

Pattern

They Gave Us Their Best

Note To Teacher: Add lines to this sheet and use for handwriting, spelling, or creative writing activities. Program the sheet with math problems, simple sentences to punctuate or capitalize, word pairs to write as contractions, or any other skill. (The African Americans shown on this sheet, from top to bottom, are Matthew Henson, Langston Hughes, Mary McLeod Bethune, Shirley Chisholm, Charles Drew, George Washington Carver, Louis Armstrong, and Marian Anderson. For more information about these people, see page 48.)

Snapshots Of Black History

Read each sentence.
Underline the letters that should be capitalized.
Then fill in the chart below.

1. martin luther king said, "i have a dream."

2. americans fought against each other in the civil war.

3. men and women were kidnapped from their homes in africa and brought to america as slaves.

4. george washington carver discovered over 300 uses for peanuts.

5. harriet tubman was a conductor on the underground railroad to canada.

Capitalize the first word in a sentence and the first word in a quotation. Also capitalize proper names and names of countries, continents, nationalities, and events.

Sentence	What did you underline?	Why?
1		
2		
3		
4		
5		

Bonus Box: Write two sentences without capital letters on the back. Ask a friend to underline the letters that should be capitalized.

  ©1990 The Education Center, Inc. • Key pp. 126–128

Mary McLeod Bethune

Many black children did not go to school when Mary was a child.
Blacks and whites went to separate schools.
There were few schools for black children.

Mary McLeod Bethune became a teacher.
She started a school for black children.
She started a college for black teachers.
She worked with the president to help blacks go to school.

Circle the wrong answers.
Write the correct answers.

1.	10 −5 — 5	2.	6 −3 — 2	3.	7 −4 — 3	4.	9 −7 — 1

5.	5 −0 — 5	6.	8 −2 — 6	7.	10 −1 — 8

8.	7 −5 — 1	9.	9 −5 — 3	10.	6 −6 — 0

Name _____

Great Contributions

Each of the famous African Americans below made important contributions to our country and to the world.

Find the four persons in the list whose most significant contributions were in the field of music. Do your work on the back of this sheet.

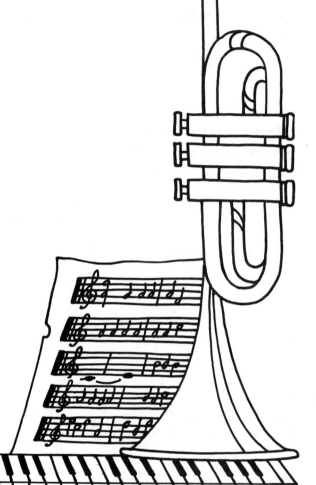

1. If 38 x 3 = 114 cross out Thurgood Marshall.
2. If 76 x 2 = 152 cross out Jesse Owens.
3. If 43 x 4 = 172 cross out Mary McLeod Bethune.
4. If 97 x 4 = 378 cross out W.C. Handy.
5. If 60 x 8 = 480 cross out Matthew Henson.
6. If 63 x 7 = 441 cross out Jesse Jackson.
7. If 18 x 9 = 162 cross out Guion Bluford.
8. If 98 x 3 = 294 cross out Jackie Robinson.
9. If 86 x 5 = 420 cross out Marian Anderson.
10. If 47 x 9 = 423 cross out Benjamin Banneker.
11. If 71 x 2 = 142 cross out Langston Hughes.
12. If 55 x 7 = 385 cross out Phillis Wheatley.
13. If 36 x 4 = 244 cross out Duke Ellington.
14. If 82 x 6 = 492 cross out Harriet Tubman.
15. If 95 x 5 = 475 cross out Daniel Hale Williams.
16. If 56 x 9 = 504 cross out Booker T. Washington.
17. If 58 x 6 = 344 cross out William Still.
18. If 91 x 4 = 364 cross out Shirley Chisholm.

Marian Anderson	Benjamin Banneker	Mary McLeod Bethune
Guion Bluford	Jackie Robinson	Shirley Chisholm
Duke Ellington	W.C. Handy	Langston Hughes
Jesse Jackson	Thurgood Marshall	Jesse Owens
Harriet Tubman	Booker T. Washington	Phillis Wheatley
Daniel Hale Williams	Matthew Henson	William Still

Bonus Box: Choose one of the persons whose name you crossed out to research. Design a poster showing that person's important contributions. Color the poster.

Happy Presidents' Day!

February is the month for presidential birthdays! Celebrate Washington's and Lincoln's birthdays on Presidents' Day (the third Monday of February) with these star-spangled activities and reproducibles.

If I Were President

After showing and discussing pictures of the White House, *Air Force One,* the presidential limousine, and other trappings of the presidency, have students discuss what life would be like as the president. Have each child illustrate one of his ideas; then display the drawings on a bulletin board decorated with magazine and newspaper pictures of the White House and the president. Have students write stories to accompany their pictures using some of these writing topics: If I were a kid in the White House…, If my daddy/mommy were president…, What the president does all day….

Presidential Pollsters

To give practice in letter writing and promote interest in American history, have your students conduct a survey of leading citizens to find out the most popular president in our country's history. Use a recent copy of *Who's Who In America* and other library resource books to compile a list of current addresses of public figures. As a class, compose a cover letter explaining the project and a questionnaire with questions such as the following:
- Which president do you think contributed the most to the history of our country?
- What important actions of this man cause him to be your favorite?
- What characteristics of this man made him a good president?

Mail the cover letter and questionnaire with a self-addressed, stamped envelope to each person on your list. You may be amazed at how many will gladly respond. What a terrific Presidents' Day project!

Dear Famous Person,
Our class is
conducting a survey
on favorite presidents.
We _____

Presidents' Day Pendants

Assist students in making presidential pendants to honor George Washington and Abraham Lincoln. Ask each child to bring a penny and a quarter from home. Stir a tablespoon of salt into a cup of vinegar until dissolved. Drop coins into the solution, allow to soak for five minutes, and rinse them off for a like-new shine. Glue red, white, and blue concentric circles (as shown) for each student. Glue a penny to one side and a quarter to the other side. Punch a hole, thread with yarn, and tie as a pendant.

Shiny Coins

For Lincoln's birthday (Feb. 12), surprise students with a shiny penny taped to each desk. Discuss the significance of the words and pictures on the penny. Have students do a "rubbing" of the penny with a crayon or pencil. On Washington's birthday (Feb. 22), have students do rubbings of quarters.

George's Favorite Dessert

Measuring and sequencing are just a bowl of cherries with this activity! Write the steps to the following recipe on cut-out Washington silhouettes (see pattern on page 57). Place the cutouts at a center for students to place in correct order. Then have small groups of students, with the help of parent volunteers, measure the ingredients and follow the steps to make George's favorite dessert!

Ingredients (serves 12):
- 6 T. butter or margarine
- 1 c. biscuit mix
- 3/4 c. sugar
- 1 c. milk
- 1/4 tsp. cinnamon
- one 21-oz. can cherry pie filling

Steps:
1. Preheat the oven to 350 degrees.
2. Place butter in a square baking dish.
3. Put the dish in the oven to melt the butter.
4. Stir the biscuit mix, sugar, milk, cinnamon, and pie filling together.
5. Pour these into the dish with the melted butter.
6. Bake for 45 minutes or until crust is done.
7. Serve warm with whipped cream.

Presidential Paper Plates

Start with a paper plate and make an unmistakable face! Provide construction paper, scissors, paste, and paper plates for students. Have children paste paper hats, hair, and beards on the plates, then draw on facial features to represent Abe Lincoln and George Washington. Mount the presidents in a row around the classroom or in the hall.

What Does Our President Do?

Young children have a difficult time understanding the job of president because it is so far removed from their lives, and they have not yet developed a sense of country. However, if the responsibilities are compared with familiar people and places, they are more easily understood. For example, discuss how the principal of your school welcomes important people who visit the school, just like the president of our country welcomes important visitors from other countries. Other presidential responsibilities to role-play or compare to familiar jobs might be: making speeches, deciding how to get along with the rest of the world, working in the Oval Office, deciding on laws we need, awarding medals, etc.

Honest Abe's QUALITY Friends

Honest Abe—Abraham Lincoln picked up that nickname during his political career. After sharing library books about Abe Lincoln and his unique personality, discuss how personal qualities can lead to nicknames. Enlarge the Lincoln silhouette on page 56 to display on the board. Enlarge and duplicate the hat pattern below on construction paper (one copy per child). Have each child write a nickname for himself on his hat cutout and mount it on the board. For an added personal touch, take a snapshot of each child to display on his hat.

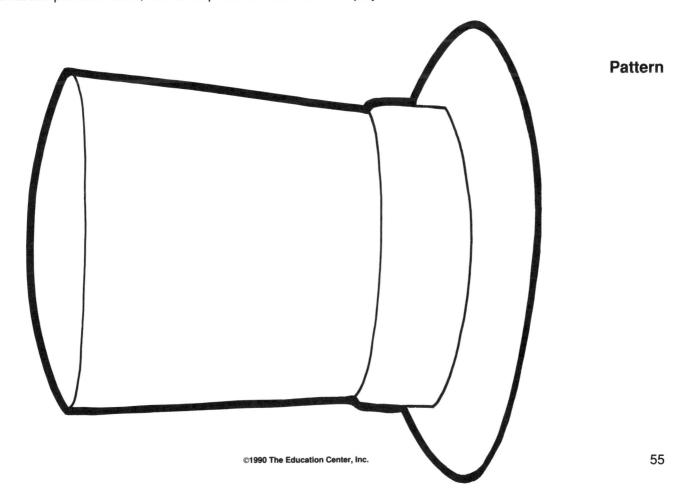

Pattern

Presidents' Day Pattern

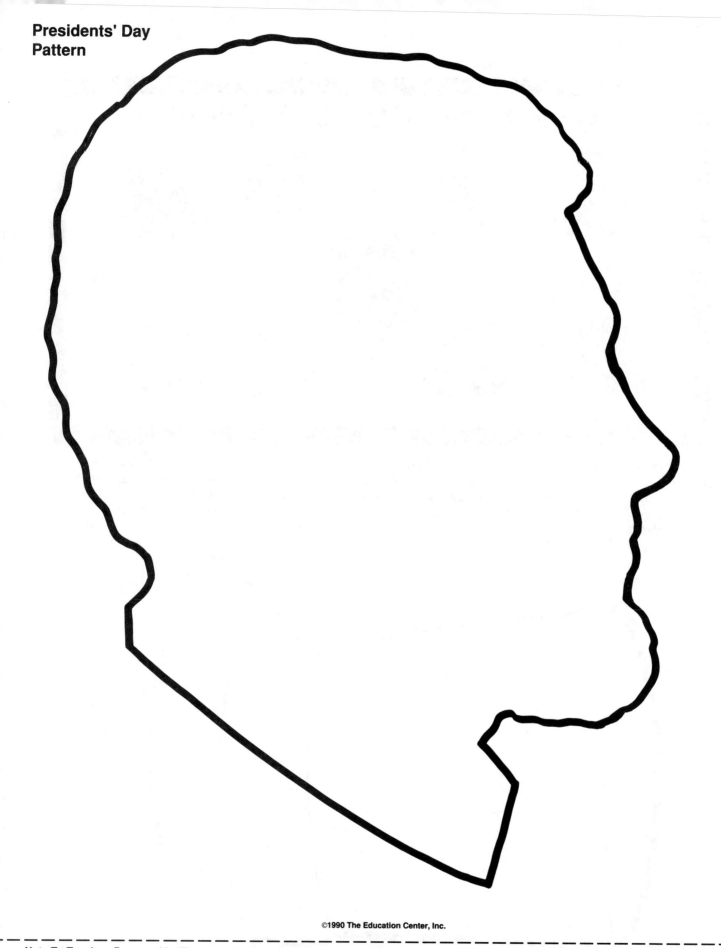

Note To Teacher: Program this silhouette with a Lincoln word search to duplicate for each child. Or have students see how many words they can list on the silhouette using only the letters in Abraham Lincoln's name. See also the activity on page 55.

©1990 The Education Center, Inc.

Note To Teacher: Duplicate this silhouette and have students trace it on notebook paper to make pages for individual booklets about Washington. Students can copy sentences or a poem about Washington, or fill the pages with original writings about our first president. Or add lines to the pattern before duplicating and have older students write paragraphs about the qualities of a great leader. See also the activity on page 54.

©1990 The Education Center, Inc.

Note To Teacher: Duplicate patterns on construction paper and cut out. Program with such skills as blend pictures/blends, math facts/answers, number words or numerals/sets, states/capitals, and uppercase/lowercase letters. Students place each wig on the matching Washington cutout. Label the backs of the cutouts for student self-checking.

Hats Off To George And Abe!

Color each hat according to the code:

Red = _____

Blue = _____

©1990 The Education Center, Inc.

Note To Teacher: Program the hats with long-/short-vowel words, correct/incorrect math facts, even/odd numbers, nouns/verbs, and other appropriate skills. Fill in the code.

George Washington's CheeriOs

Write an O in each word that has the **short o** sound.
Glue a CheeriO in each word with the **long o** sound.
Eat the extra CheeriOs!

h_____pe   b_____ne

b_____x

_____ld   ch_____p

s_____ck   r_____se

m_____p

c_____ld   kn_____w

c_____at   s_____ap

n_____t

sn_____w   b_____wl

_____n   st_____p

n_____se

gr_____w   g_____

©1990 The Education Center, Inc. • Key pp. 126–128

Note To Teacher: Provide students with CheeriOs breakfast cereal and glue.

George Or Abe?

Circle the letter under the president described in each phrase.
Write the letters in the numbered blanks below.

	George Washington	Abraham Lincoln
1. Born in a log cabin in Hardin County, Kentucky	A	O
2. Rode a horse or ferry to school every day	N	C
3. Favorite pastime was reading	D	V
4. Became a lawyer	S	H
5. Traveled through wild country to survey land	R	U
6. Led an army in the Revolutionary War	E	N
7. Spoke out against slavery	L	I
8. Helped United States gain freedom from England	O	F
9. Known as the "Father Of Our Country"	S	M
10. Was president during the Civil War	A	C
11. Was assassinated in 1865	P	I
12. Face found on the penny	W	R
13. Face found on the quarter	O	G
14. Was our first president	R	E

George Washington had lost nearly all of his own teeth by the time he was 57.
What were his false teeth made from?

___ ___ ___ ___ ___ ___ ___ ___ ___ ___   ___ ___ ___ ___ **Y**
14 4   7   2   13 10 6   12 1   9   11 3   8   5

Name _____

Presidents' Day Puzzler

On each silhouette, list as many words as you can using the letters in that president's name.
Use the back of this sheet if you need more space.

**GEORGE
WASHINGTON**

**ABRAHAM
LINCOLN**

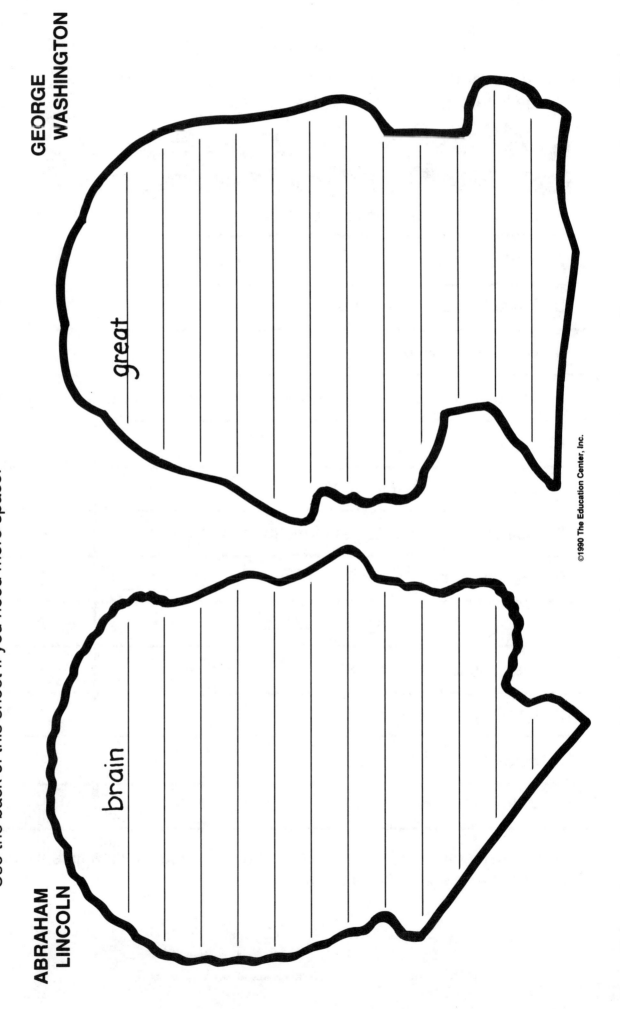

great

brain

©1990 The Education Center, Inc.

St. Patrick's Day Shenanigans

Capture the magical quality of St. Patrick's Day with the following delightful activities.

Magic Dust And Such

Begin your day with a visit from an elusive leprechaun and close in on the mysterious little guy as the day draws to an end. It's the perfect way to celebrate this lively day!

● Discovering and following a leprechaun's trail of magic dust is a great way to begin St. Patrick's Day. Before the children arrive, open one of the windows in the classroom and sprinkle some green glitter on the windowsill. Make a trail of glitter that leads to a closet or other good hiding place. When the children arrive, tell them that you suspect a mysterious leprechaun has visited the classroom. If your class can catch him, they can have his pot of gold. Intermittently, pretend to have seen a flash of green whiz by. No doubt, some of your students will have seen it, too!

● Your youngsters will delight in discovering that a leprechaun has visited their classroom during their absence. While your class is at lunch or recess, have a colleague overturn a few chairs, turn some coats inside out, and generally mix up a few things in your classroom. Provide some St. Patrick's Day stickers for her to attach to children's belongings. Ask her to write a message for the children on the chalkboard using green chalk. The children may be disappointed to have just missed the leprechaun, but they will take great pleasure in his visit nevertheless. Turn this trick into a terrific writing opportunity by having students write letters to the mischievous leprechaun.

Pattern

● Conclude your St. Patrick's Day shenanigans by closing in on your mysterious leprechaun visitor. In advance, write a series of clues on shamrock-shaped cutouts (pattern on page 71) and hide them in your classroom or building. Arrange for the clues to lead to a black kettle filled with coin-shaped candy. Serve shamrock-shaped cookies and lemonade tinted with green food coloring. Present each child with a badge stating that he was visited by a leprechaun. Wouldn't you love to hear your students as they recount this lively day of leprechaun chasing?

student

was visited by a leprechaun today!

Saved By The Shamrocks

The minute your students enter the classroom on St. Patrick's Day, hand them 3" x 4" pieces of green construction paper and shamrock patterns (see page 71). As the students trace and cut out their shamrocks, distribute stickers and safety pins. Have everyone mount their stickers on the shamrocks and then pin the cutouts onto their clothing. In this way, everyone can participate in wearing a bit of the green on this special day!

Yummy Shamrocks

For a green treat that's hard to beat, mix up a batch of yummy shamrocks!

Ingredients:
35 marshmallows
1 stick margarine
1 tsp. vanilla
3 cups cornflakes
1 tsp. green food coloring

Steps:
1. Melt the marshmallows and margarine in the top of a double boiler.
2. Add vanilla, coloring, and cornflakes.
3. After cooling slightly, form shamrocks on small sheets of waxed paper.
4. Add green candy sprinkles if desired.

Pattern

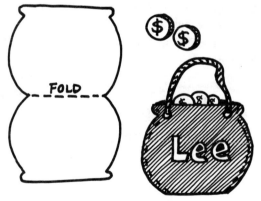

FOLD

Lee

Pots Of Gold

Let a little leprechaun gold motivate your students to complete their assignments. At the beginning of March, give each child a pattern to trace, cut out, fold, and staple to make his own pot. Punch a hole on each side of the pot, attach yarn for a handle, and hang from the chalkboard ledge. Duplicate a supply of gold coins on yellow construction paper.

As each child finishes an assignment, give him a paper coin to put in his pot. On St. Patrick's Day, have everyone count and turn in his coins for a special reward. With this incentive, your leprechauns will keep working right up to Easter vacation!

Shamrock Pie

Have you ever made a Shamrock Pie? It's easy and educational at the same time! Cut sponges into shamrock shapes and place each in a plastic dish. Sprinkle the sponges generously with birdseed or grass seed; then pour water into each dish. If kept moist, the seeds will sprout in a week or so.

Lucky You—St. Patrick's Day Games!

Shamrock Concentration

Make a versatile shamrock gameboard and use it to practice a variety of skills. Cut a large shamrock from green poster board (pattern on page 71). Draw 24 circles on the gameboard. Label 12 wooden or paper disks with contractions. Label 12 other disks with the words forming each contraction.

To play, place all the disks facedown on the gameboard, one disk per circle. In turn, each player turns over two disks. If they match, the player keeps the disks and takes another turn. If there is no match, the disks are turned back over and it is the next player's turn. The player with the most disks at the end of the game wins.

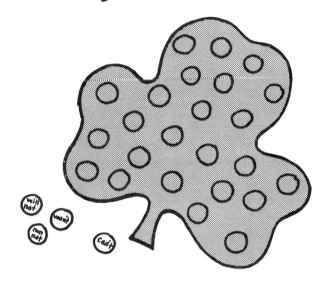

Around The Shamrock

Use this St. Patrick's Day gameboard to review multiplication facts. Cut a shamrock shape from green poster board. Draw a trail game around the edge. Provide a deck of multiplication flash cards, a die, and game markers. Write each flash card's answer on the back of the card.

Each student rolls the die and moves his marker that number of spaces. He then draws a multiplication card and says the product. If correct, he rolls and moves again. If incorrect, his turn is finished. Play continues until one player goes all around the shamrock.

$$3 \times 5 \quad \rightarrow \quad 15$$

Shamrock Spelling

Add some seasonal flavoring to spelling word practice. Have one student select a word from the spelling list. He then uses it aloud in a sentence, substituting the word *shamrock* for the regular spelling word. The child who guesses the missing word and spells it correctly is the next player.

Shamrock Rock

Reinforce basic number concepts with this small group game. Cut out and laminate a green, construction paper shamrock for each player (pattern on page 71). Write a different number on each cutout; then place the shamrocks facedown on a table. While Irish music is playing, have children march around the table. When the music stops, each player picks up a shamrock. The child with the lowest number is out. Continue playing until one child is left. For older students, write math facts on the shamrocks. The student with the lowest answer in each round is eliminated.

St. Patrick's Day Art Projects

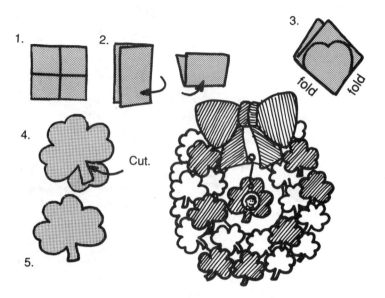

Irish Eyes Are Smiling

Invite the luck of the Irish with lovely, student-made shamrock wreaths. Cut away the center of a thin paper plate. Cover the rim of the plate with various shades of green shamrock cutouts. (Cut shamrocks from folded paper as shown.) Glue your picture to another shamrock cutout, and use string to suspend this shamrock from the rim of the plate. Add a bow to complete the wreath. Display these wreaths with the caption, "Irish Eyes Are Smilin'."

Lucky Leprechauns

Challenge each of your students to transform a paper plate into a lively leprechaun. Provide a variety of markers and construction paper and yarn scraps for students to use to make their leprechauns' hats, eyes, noses, hair, pipes, mouths, and eyebrows. Let students glue on green crepe paper whiskers for a whimsical finishing touch.

Snaky Masterpieces

Let this fun art project entice your students to learn about snakes. Tell the legend of St. Patrick driving the snakes from Ireland; then give each child a 9" x 12" piece of white construction paper. Have the child draw a random design on his paper with a pencil, then fill in each space with a bright color of crayon or marker. When the page is completely filled with color, have the student turn his paper over and trace a wiggly snake on the back. After cutting out the snake, have the student mount it on a green piece of construction paper. To finish these colorful projects, have each child glue a wiggle eye to his snake. Display the projects on a "Sneakin' Up On Snakes" bulletin board. Challenge your students to write facts about snakes on cut-out shamrocks to post with their masterpieces.

Dancing Shamrocks

Fill your room with student-made shamrock mobiles, and then watch as the shamrocks dance in the breeze. You will need several sizes of shamrock-shaped tracers. From green construction paper, cut one large and three small shamrock shapes. Attach the smaller shamrocks to the larger one using string and tape. Then cut green wallpaper shapes to fit inside the construction paper ones. Glue the wallpaper shamrocks in place. Happy St. Patrick's Day!

Wild Shamrocks

Using the pattern on page 71, duplicate a shamrock on white construction paper for each student. Have students use a variety of bright crayons or oil pastels to color all of the page except the shamrock. Provide large brushes and green tempera paint. Students paint the entire page. Since crayon and oil pastels will resist the paint, a green shamrock will appear.

Capture The Leprechaun

You've got to be clever to catch a leprechaun! But your youngsters will be anxious to try to nab these little Irish elves. Provide toilet tissue tubes, various colors of construction paper, markers, small plastic berry baskets, shredded tissue paper (or cellophane "grass"), scissors, glue, and poster board. To make a leprechaun, cut and glue construction paper clothing, hands, and facial features on half a tissue tube. Add details with markers. Place the elf on a bed of paper grass and put him inside a berry basket. Glue the berry basket to half of a sheet of poster board as shown. On a copy of the open worksheet on page 74, write an account of how the captive elf was nabbed. Complete the project by attaching the story and some shamrock cutouts to the poster board.

For variety, glue the leprechaun inside two berry baskets, and suspend the imprisoned elf from the ceiling using yarn.

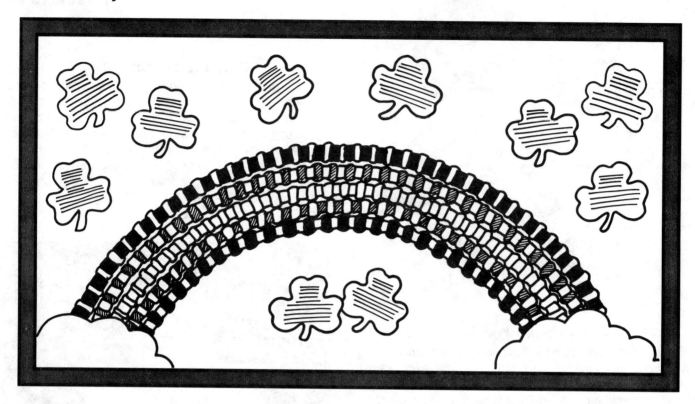

Brighten a hallway or classroom with a colorful display made entirely by students. Have children make a giant rainbow using construction paper chains. Display original writings on cut-out shamrocks (pattern on page 71). Your students will have lots of luck getting started writing if you post these ideas: When I found the pot of gold at the end of the rainbow…; Catching a leprechaun is hard work!…; I knew it was going to be a special St. Patrick's Day when…; I needed some good luck the day that I…. Add some fluffy, paper or cotton clouds.

A giant reptile is just the thing to sharpen research skills! Share the legend of St. Patrick driving the snakes from Ireland. Have students use resource books to draw detailed, pencil sketches of snakes to post on the board. Add a large snake around the edges of the board for a display that's sure to turn heads!

How About A Shamrock Shake?

Use the patterns below and on page 71 to create a working bulletin board that's just right for March. Number 12 to 16 paper shamrocks and label them with math facts, short-/long-vowel words, or sentences to punctuate. Have students work on the problems on their own paper during free time. Reward each child who answers a certain number of problems correctly with a "shamrock shake." To make, add a dash of mint extract and green food coloring to a vanilla milk shake. To vary, reprogram the shamrocks with new problems each day until March 17. Award a shake to those children who have attempted all of the problems.

Pattern

Enlarge and use with the bulletin board on this page.

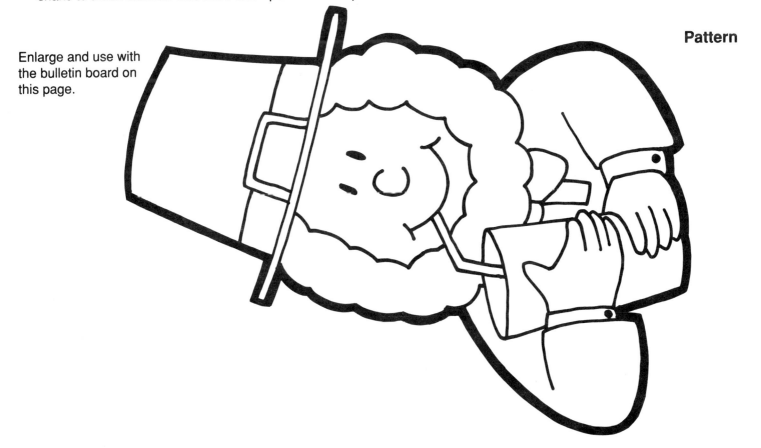

St. Patrick's Day Learning Centers

Shamrock Sampling

A giant, poster board shamrock will make a super wall display and a stimulating language arts center. Label the shamrock with a St. Patrick's Day word list (see illustration). Write the following tasks on cut-out shamrocks (pattern on page 71). Store the task cards in a paper pocket glued to the front of the shamrock.

Tasks:

- Put the words in alphabetical order.
- Define eight of the words.
- Illustrate five of the words.
- Write three sentences using as many of the words as you can.
- Write a St. Patrick's Day story using six of the words.
- Divide seven of the words into syllables.
- Write rhyming words for nine of the words.
- Make a crossword puzzle using eight of the words.

Blarney Pudding

A leprechaun's secret recipe provides practice in following directions and working independently. Set up enough materials so all of your students can try Blarney Pudding. Write the steps on a green piece of poster board and display at a center with the materials. Ask a parent volunteer to man your center so that small groups can rotate through at intervals. *Magic Moo* is actually milk, while the *Magic Powder* is instant pistachio pudding (or substitute vanilla pudding and add green food coloring).

Blarney Pudding

1. Pour 1/4 cup Magic Moo into a baby food jar.
2. Add one tablespoon of Magic Powder.
3. Screw the lid on the jar carefully.
4. Shake the jar well until the pudding is thick.
5. Remove the lid and enjoy!

The Greens Have It!

Provide plenty of graphing practice with an activity that focuses on your students. Take a class poll to complete a graph similar to the one shown; then display the graph at a center with a set of questions for students to answer using the graph.

1. How many students are represented on the graph in all?
2. Is there any category with no students listed?
3. How many students like lime Jell-O?
4. Are there more students who have eaten mint candy or who have green shirts on?
5. How many students have green eyes?
6. Which are there more of: green-eyed students or lucky students?
7. Is green a popular color in our class?
8. Which categories have the same number of students listed in them?

The Greens Have It!	✤ = two students
Students who like the color green	✤
Students who have green eyes	✤✤
Students who have green shirts on	✤✤✤✤
Students who like lime Jell-O	✤
Students who have eaten mint candy	✤✤✤
Students who have a dollar bill	✤✤✤✤✤
Students who have found a four-leaf clover	✤

A

Staple
over
B.

Cut here.

Cut here.

B

Note To Teacher: Duplicate on green construction paper. Have students cut, decorate, and staple to secure.

When Irish Eyes Are Smiling

Sack Of Potato Answers

Note To Teacher: Program the potatoes with math problems, review questions, words to abbreviate, or other appropriate skills. Write the answers in the potato sack. Write student directions at the top of the worksheet. The student solves each problem and crosses off the answer in the potato sack as he uses it.

Note To Teacher: Duplicate this open sheet to use for assignments, tests, creative writing, or a holiday newsletter. See "Capture The Leprechaun" on page 67 for a way to use this sheet.

Leprechaun Savings

Help the leprechaun count his money.
Write each amount with $ and .
The first one is done for you.

3 dollars
75 cents

$3.75

1 dollar
1 dime

_____

8 dollars
43 cents

_____

4 dollars
67 cents

_____

5 dollars
7 cents

_____

5 dollars
2 quarters

_____

9 dollars
19 cents

_____

6 dollars
89 cents

_____

9 dollars
1 nickel

_____

2 dollars
1 quarter

_____

7 dollars
2 cents

_____

3 dollars
7 dimes

_____

Bonus Box: Color the coin with the greatest value **red**.
Color the coin with the least value **blue**.
Color two coins with a sum of $8.77 **yellow**.

©1990 The Education Center, Inc. • Key pp. 126–128

Name _____

Lucky Leprechaun

Help the leprechaun find his pot of gold.
Color the path only where the answers
are correct.

START

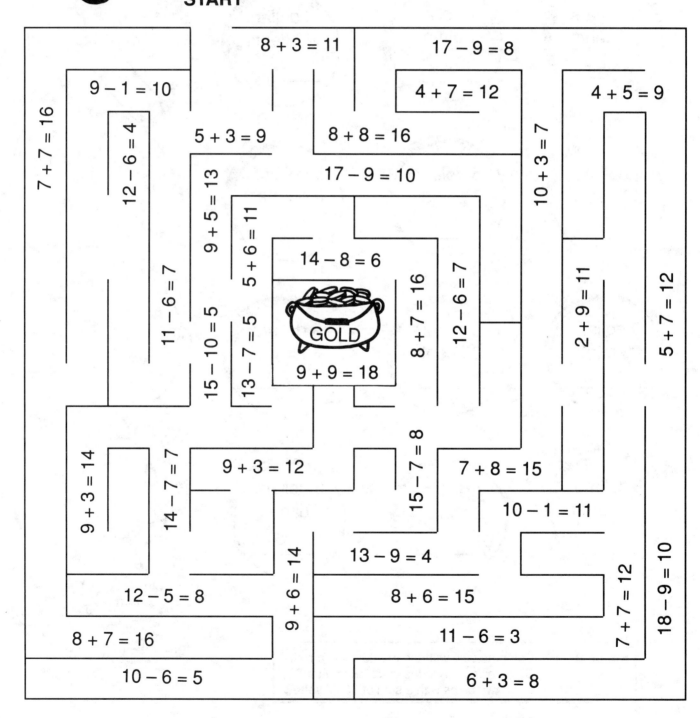

8 + 3 = 11

17 − 9 = 8

9 − 1 = 10

4 + 7 = 12

4 + 5 = 9

7 + 7 = 16

12 − 6 = 4

5 + 3 = 9

8 + 8 = 16

10 + 3 = 7

17 − 9 = 10

9 + 5 = 13

5 + 6 = 11

14 − 8 = 6

11 − 6 = 7

8 + 7 = 16

12 − 6 = 7

2 + 9 = 11

5 + 7 = 12

15 − 10 = 5

13 − 7 = 5

GOLD

9 + 9 = 18

9 + 3 = 14

14 − 7 = 7

9 + 3 = 12

15 − 7 = 8

7 + 8 = 15

10 − 1 = 11

13 − 9 = 4

9 + 6 = 14

8 + 6 = 15

7 + 7 = 12

18 − 9 = 10

12 − 5 = 8

8 + 7 = 16

11 − 6 = 3

10 − 6 = 5

6 + 3 = 8

Golden Words

Write a synonym for each word in the blanks.
Use a thesaurus to help you.

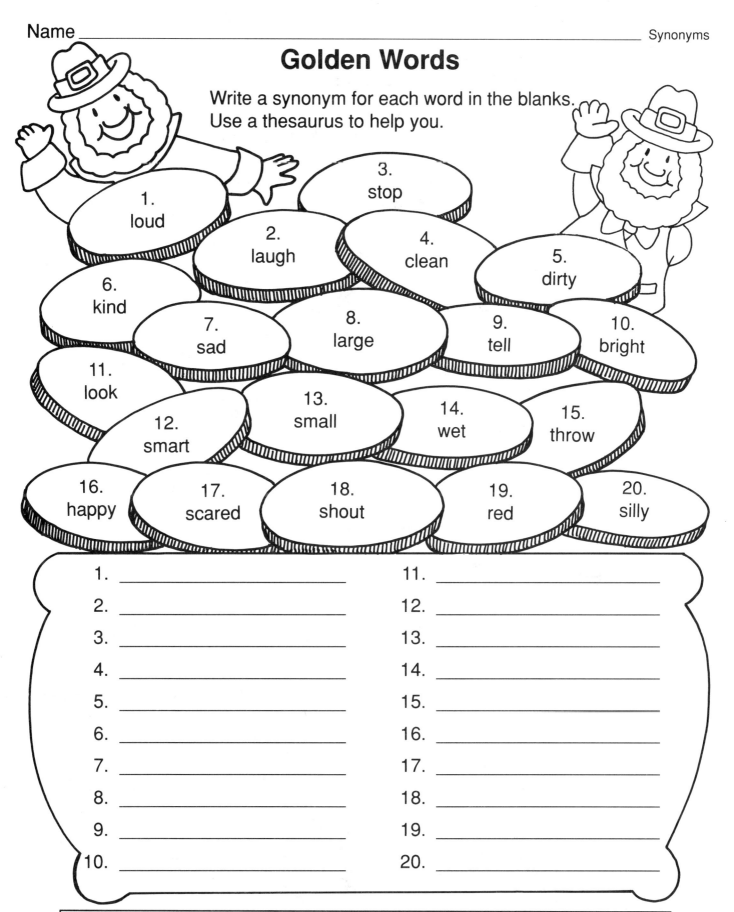

1. loud
2. laugh
3. stop
4. clean
5. dirty
6. kind
7. sad
8. large
9. tell
10. bright
11. look
12. smart
13. small
14. wet
15. throw
16. happy
17. scared
18. shout
19. red
20. silly

1. _____
2. _____
3. _____
4. _____
5. _____
6. _____
7. _____
8. _____
9. _____
10. _____

11. _____
12. _____
13. _____
14. _____
15. _____
16. _____
17. _____
18. _____
19. _____
20. _____

Bonus Box: You've just been asked to deliver a pot of gold to the person you admire the most in the world. Write a paragraph describing why that person deserves a pot of gold. Use three of the words you listed above.

Spring Is In The Air!

Bright sunshine, soft rain showers, budding flowers, warmer weather—spring is here!
Welcome this lovely season with the following pages of springtime activities and ideas.

**Decorate your room in time to celebrate spring with these
easy-to-use ideas.**

The Springtime Tree

Celebrate the coming of spring with a student-made display. Plant a bare tree branch in a weighted can or bucket. Have students glue green and pink tissue paper on the branches to create a springtime tree. Next have students make flower art projects. Mount each flower on a green poster board stem, and insert it in a colorful, weighted cup. Place the flowers around the tree. Have students add other props to complete the springtime effect.

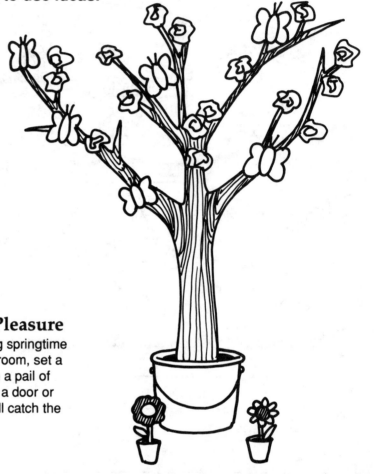

Pinwheel Pleasure

For an appealing springtime decoration in your room, set a colorful pinwheel in a pail of sand. Place it near a door or window where it will catch the breeze.

Springtime Borders

Here's a bulletin board border that's fast, easy, and perfect for springtime displays! Cut several colors of tissue paper into 1/2" x 12" strips. Mix the colored strips together; then staple small handfuls of strips around the edges of a bulletin board. Try mixing hot pink, blue, bright yellow, and green for a spectacular springtime border.

Spring's Super Spellers

Spring Is Planting Time

Two Unusual Gardens

• Grow some green hair for spring! Have each child draw a face on a Styrofoam cup. Add potting soil, grass seed, and water to each cup. By the end of the week, your bald-headed men will have grown "hair"! By the next week, your fellows will need haircuts, so send the cups home with your excited children.

• Put a clean, empty eggshell half in each section of an egg carton. Fill each eggshell with potting soil and a few marigold or other flower seeds. Add a little more soil and place in a sunny window. Keep the soil damp. After the flowers sprout, have students carefully transfer the plants outside to create a pleasant garden spot for your school.

A Garden Plot

Your gardeners will find plenty of tasks to keep them busy at this garden plot. As a class, brainstorm a list of 15 (or half the number of students in your classroom) vegetables. Provide students with 3" x 4" sheets of white construction paper and one Popsicle stick for every two students. In pairs, each student draws, colors, and labels one side of a seed packet for a common vegetable. Each student pair then glues their drawings and Popsicle stick together as shown. Stand the completed seed packets at a center in a large box filled with sand. Have students use the vegetable names in the garden plot to complete one or more of the following activities: write the names in alphabetical order, write the plural form of each name, divide each name into syllables, write a riddle for each name, write three adjectives to describe each name, create a recipe using one of the vegetables as a main ingredient.

Spring Watering

Water seeds and seedlings with tender, loving care using two Styrofoam cups. Poke several small holes in the bottom of one cup. Fill the other cup with water. Hold the cup bearing holes over the soil to be watered; then pour the water (from the other cup) into this cup. The water will gently rain over the soil, preventing eroding soil or broken seedlings.

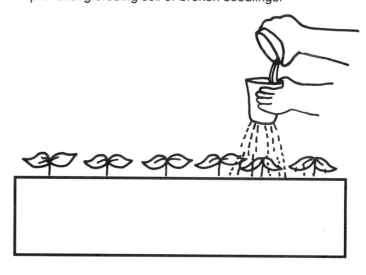

Dirt Dessert

After a lesson on spring planting, serve Dirt Dessert from a plastic, 23" x 6" x 6" flower tray. Use a small plastic shovel or spade to dish out the "dirt." Place gummy worms on top of the "dirt" and watch your kids dig in!

Ingredients:

1 large package Oreo cookies
12-oz. container of Cool Whip
8 oz. cream cheese (softened)
1 cup powdered sugar

1 stick margarine (softened)
2 cups milk
3-oz. box of French vanilla pudding
1 tsp. vanilla

Crush Oreos and place half in the bottom of the tray (or an 11" x 17" pan). Save the rest of the crushed cookies for the top. Use a mixer to blend Cool Whip, cream cheese, powdered sugar, and margarine. In a bowl, combine pudding, milk, and vanilla. Beat this mixture until it's the consistency of pudding. Combine both mixtures and pour over the layer of crushed Oreos. Sprinkle the remaining Oreos on top. Refrigerate until serving time.

Let's Go Fly A Kite!
High-flyin' Kite Activities

Add A Tail

Create a kite that extends across a chalkboard sky. Each day draw a kite with a very long tail that snakes across the chalkboard. On the kite, write instructions to students indicating the kind of tail needed, such as "Long *o* words" or "Facts That Equal 10." During the day, students come up to the board and draw bows with correct words or facts. Check all answers at the end of the day for a quick class review.

A Colorful Kite

Here's a kite that will have your students flying high over color words! Mount a large kite cutout sporting a yarn tail on your bulletin board or wall. When your youngsters can identify a color word, add a bow of that color to the kite tail. (For older students, attach a bow for each class goal met, each book read, or each day of perfect attendance.) You'll soon have a colorful display and a group of very proud children!

Flying Free Time Activities

Sail into spring with a bulletin board full of free-time activities. Mount blue and green background paper on a board to resemble the sky and a green lawn. Have students illustrate and cut out pictures of themselves to put on the board. Attach kite cutouts labeled with free-time activities to the illustrations. Plan an afternoon of kite making and kite flying for students who complete a designated number of activities.

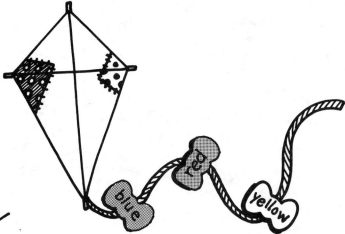

Kite Trains

Kite systems put several kites up into the air in a train. In 1978, a Japanese kite flier lofted 4,128 kites on one string with the highest kite 4,266 feet in the sky! Have students launch their own kite train of words by placing vocabulary or spelling words in alphabetical order. Write words on kite shapes for children to clip to a kite string suspended at a center. Alphabetizing will be a breeze!

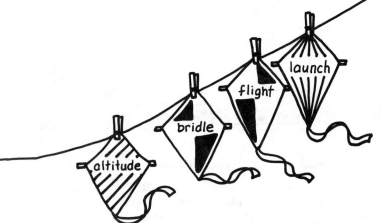

Springtime Art Activities

Snap, Crackle, And Poppin' Pictures

Create three-dimensional March lions and lambs that make terrific open house invitations. Fold white and gold construction paper in half and cut a simple body shape from each as shown. Cut out a white or gold circle for each animal's head. Add facial features with markers before gluing on the circles. Attach paper ears to the lamb and tails to both animals. For the finishing touch, glue on rice cereal to make the lion's mane and popped popcorn for the lamb's "wool." Add a little rice cereal to the lion's tail as well. What fun!

Blooming Beauties

A splash of colorful blooms is just what you need to create a sunny atmosphere. Pour a thin layer of yellow tempera paint in one pie pan, and orange in another. Clip a six-inch length of string or yarn to each of two clothespins. Holding one clothespin, drag the string through the yellow paint. Swirl and drag the string on a sheet of 12-inch-square art paper. Repeat using the other string and the orange paint. When the paper is dry, fold the painting twice and cut as shown. For a three-dimensional bulletin board display, pin each "bloom" through the center only. Then pin on circular centers, and add construction paper vines and leaves.

Transparent Kites

Add splashes of color to your springtime classroom with these unusual, see-through kites. Have each student cut two, open, kite shapes from construction paper using a tagboard pattern. Then have students draw and cut out construction paper scenes for their kites. Arrange and sandwich the designs between laminating film, clear Con-Tact covering, or waxed paper. Students glue the transparent designs between the kite frames and trim to fit. Add yarn hangers and tails to complete the effect. Hang these kites where they are likely to be brushed by a gentle breeze.

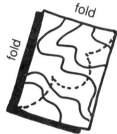

SPRING BEAUTIES

No More "Lion"...Baaaah!

No "lion"! "Ewe" and your students are going to love this art project that doubles as a spring bulletin board. Using the patterns on page 83 as tracers, cut out a sheep's face, ears, and legs from black construction paper. Cut two, 1" white circles and two, 3/4" black circles for eyes. Glue the smaller circles atop the larger ones, and glue them to the sheep face cutout. Glue the face cutout to a thin, white, luncheon-size paper plate, before gluing the ear cutouts to the back side of the plate. Glue the small plate to a larger plate as shown, and glue the legs to the back of the larger plate. "Ewe" will have conjured up everything but the "baaaah" when you add a fluffy cotton ball tail to the larger plate. (See the bulletin board on page 86 for a suggested display.)

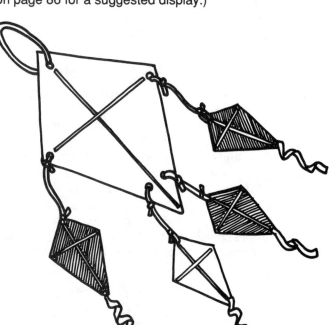

Blowing In The Breeze

As the first blustery blasts of spring come through your classroom windows, these kite mobiles will dance in the breeze. Provide a large kite-shaped pattern (nine inches tall) and a smaller kite-shaped pattern (six inches tall). To make the mobile, trace one large and four small kites on construction paper and cut them out. Fold the large kite along the length and breadth; then unfold. Using the fold lines as guides, punch holes in the large kite where indicated. Glue uncooked spaghetti "frames" on all kites. Use yarn to connect and suspend the kites. Add tissue or cellophane tails to complete the kite mobiles.

Springtime Sun Catchers

Brighten up your classroom this spring with student-made sun catchers.

Materials: assorted colors of tissue paper, plastic wrap, white glue, yarn, scissors, tape, small pieces of cardboard, paintbrushes

Procedure:
1. Tear or cut tissue paper into small pieces.
2. Tape a piece of plastic wrap to a piece of cardboard.
3. Paint an area of the plastic with white glue.
4. Lay pieces of tissue on the glue, overlapping the pieces. Carefully paint over the tissue with white glue. Allow to dry overnight.
5. Peel tissue paper away from the plastic wrap. Cut out a design such as a flower or kite. Glue yarn around the edge and in the center as shown.
6. Add a loop at the top and hang in a window. Let the sun shine through!

GLUE

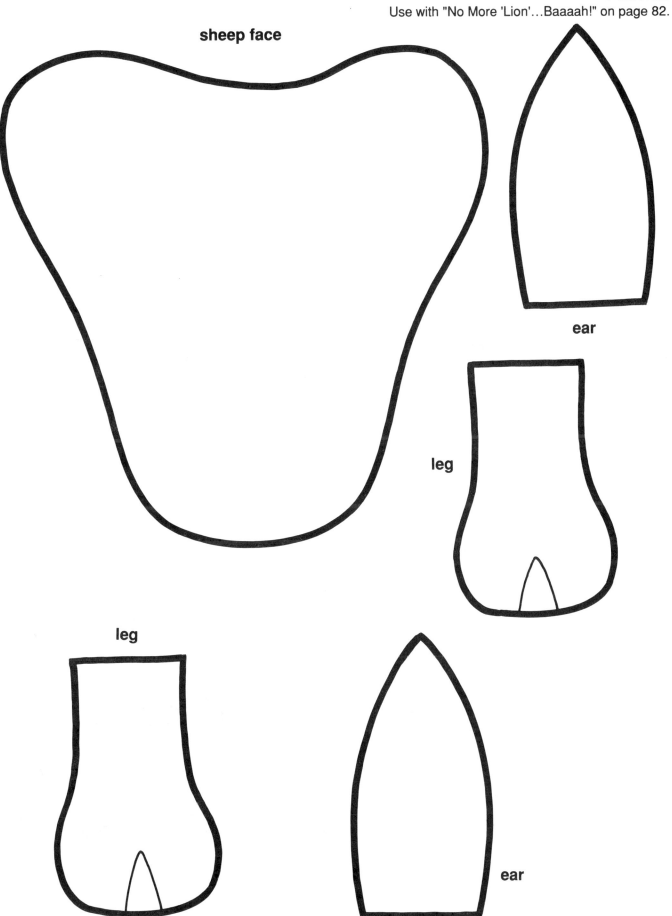

sheep face

ear

leg

leg

ear

Welcome spring with a three-dimensional bulletin board. Have each child cut out a flower shape from yellow construction paper. The student then glues a yellow cupcake liner in the center of his flower cutout. After adding paper stems and leaves, you'll have a field of flowers for a lovely display!

When blustery, kite-flying weather arrives, display your students' favorite work samples on this becoming bulletin board. Cut out a white, butcher paper cloud, and attach it to blue background paper before drawing on a facial expression and breezy swirls. Staple a favorite paper of each student to the board atop a sheet of construction paper. Have students make construction paper kites complete with yarn tails and fabric ties. Attach the kites to the board near their work samples.

Put out the welcome mat for spring with this eye-catching door display. Cut out a large paper umbrella and mount it on your classroom door. Have students make paper flowers, butterflies, birds, and other signs of spring to insert in and around the umbrella.

Spring Chicks

Hatch a spring bulletin board that's ready to program with a variety of skills. Duplicate the patterns on page 87 on white and yellow construction paper. After cutting out and laminating, use a wipe-off marker to program the chicks and eggs with math facts/answers, beginning consonants/pictures, vocabulary words/definitions, antonyms, homonyms, or any other skill. Children fit each chick inside the correct shell. When you're ready to use the display to practice a different skill, simply wipe the cutouts off and reprogram.

Celebrate the arrival of spring with this amusing display. Using the instructions (page 82) and the patterns (page 83), have students create paper plate lambs. Add interest to the lion cutout (pattern on page 87) by having students loosely wrap construction paper strips around their pencils, then unwrap the strips and glue them to the lion's mane. Now what are "ewe" waiting for?

Plant a spring garden on a bulletin board! Have each student moisten a paper towel and place it in a plastic sandwich bag. Sprinkle several seeds between each paper towel and bag. Staple all of the bags to the board (seed side showing). Your students will enjoy watching their seeds sprout and grow.

Use the chick and egg patterns with "Spring Chicks" on page 85.

Enlarge the lion pattern to use with "No More 'Lion'..." on page 86.

Springtime Learning Centers

Guide Word Garden

Plant a garden of guide word practice! Make flowers by gluing bright, construction paper cutouts to Popsicle sticks. Write a word on each "stem." Write guide word pairs on soup cans that have been covered with paper or adhesive covering. Your young gardeners place each flower in the correct can.

Spring Name Clouds

Try this personalized creative writing activity when spring arrives. Cut out a white cloud shape for each student in your class. Glue the clouds in several blue file folders. Label each cloud with a student's name written vertically as shown and laminate. After thinking about the characteristics of spring, have the students use a wipe-off marker to write favorite phrases about the season to go with each letter in their names. Make this a pass-around-the-room project, or use as an individual activity at a center.

Spring Vacation

Pack your bags and get ready for a spring vacation like no other! Label the backs of four picture postcards as shown. Store the cards and a die in a small travel bag with items such as a bottle of suntan lotion, a spare toothbrush, an old plane ticket or set of car keys, and other vacation objects. Display finished stories on a "What A Spring Vacation!" bulletin board or bind together in a class book.

Directions:
1. Roll the die once to find your destination.
2. Roll again to find your traveling companion.
3. Roll again to find your type of transportation.
4. Use these items to write about your unusual vacation.

COMPANION
1. Wizard of Oz
2. a mermaid
3. Blackbeard the pirate
4. Tom Sawyer
5. a tiny elf
6. your favorite star

DESTINATION
1. a Hawaiian island
2. an abandoned cave
3. a castle in Europe
4. the North Pole
5. a colonial time
6. an alien planet

TRANSPORTATION
1. spaceship
2. hot-air balloon
3. submarine
4. magic carpet
5. jet-pack
6. elephant caravan

Sheepish Synonyms

Take a leap into synonym practice! Duplicate six or more copies of the patterns below on white construction paper. After coloring the bows with markers, cut out the sheep. Glue them inside a colorful file folder and label with words. Laminate; then have students use a wipe-off marker to label the bows with matching synonyms. Use the patterns to make additional folders to practice addition and subtraction, rhyming words, antonyms, or contractions.

Patterns

89

Spring
March Lion Patterns

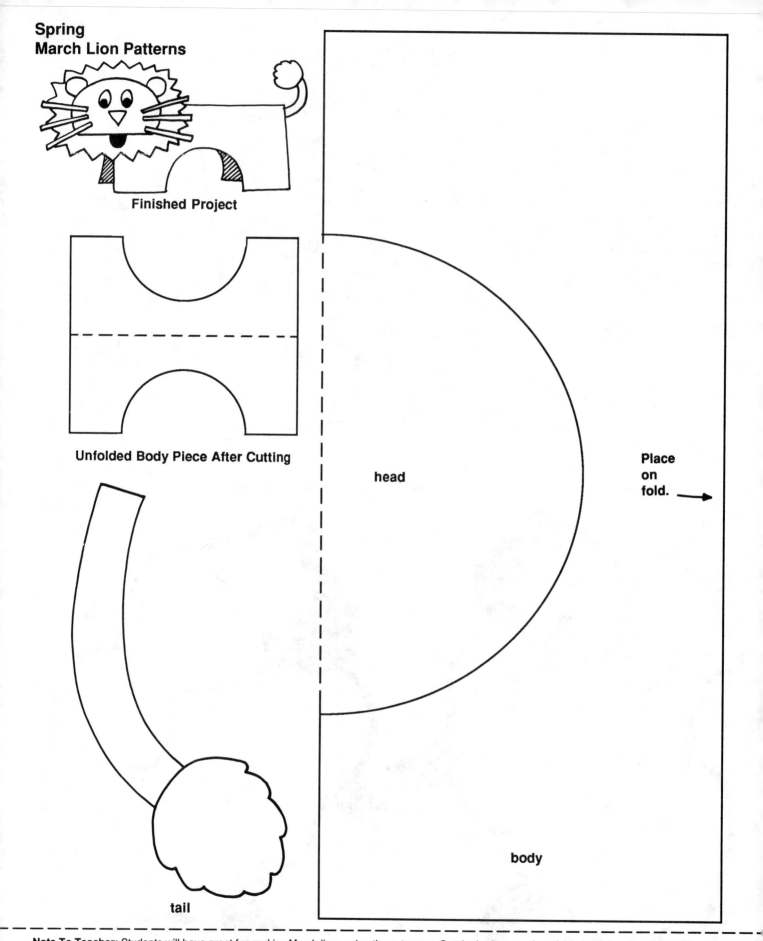

Finished Project

Unfolded Body Piece After Cutting

tail

head

body

Place on fold. →

Spring Cleaning

1.

2.

3.

4.

5.

6.

7.

8.

9.

10.

11.

12.

©1990 The Education Center, Inc.

Note To Teacher: Program clothes on lines with math problems, words to define, review questions, etc. Label clothes basket with answers. Add directions at the top.

Name _____

Spring Into Spring!!!

Note To Teacher: Duplicate this open worksheet for newsletters, spelling tests, creative writing, or poetry. If desired, add lines before duplication.

Kites Away!

Write the plural for each word on a kite tail.
Then circle your answers in the word search to check.

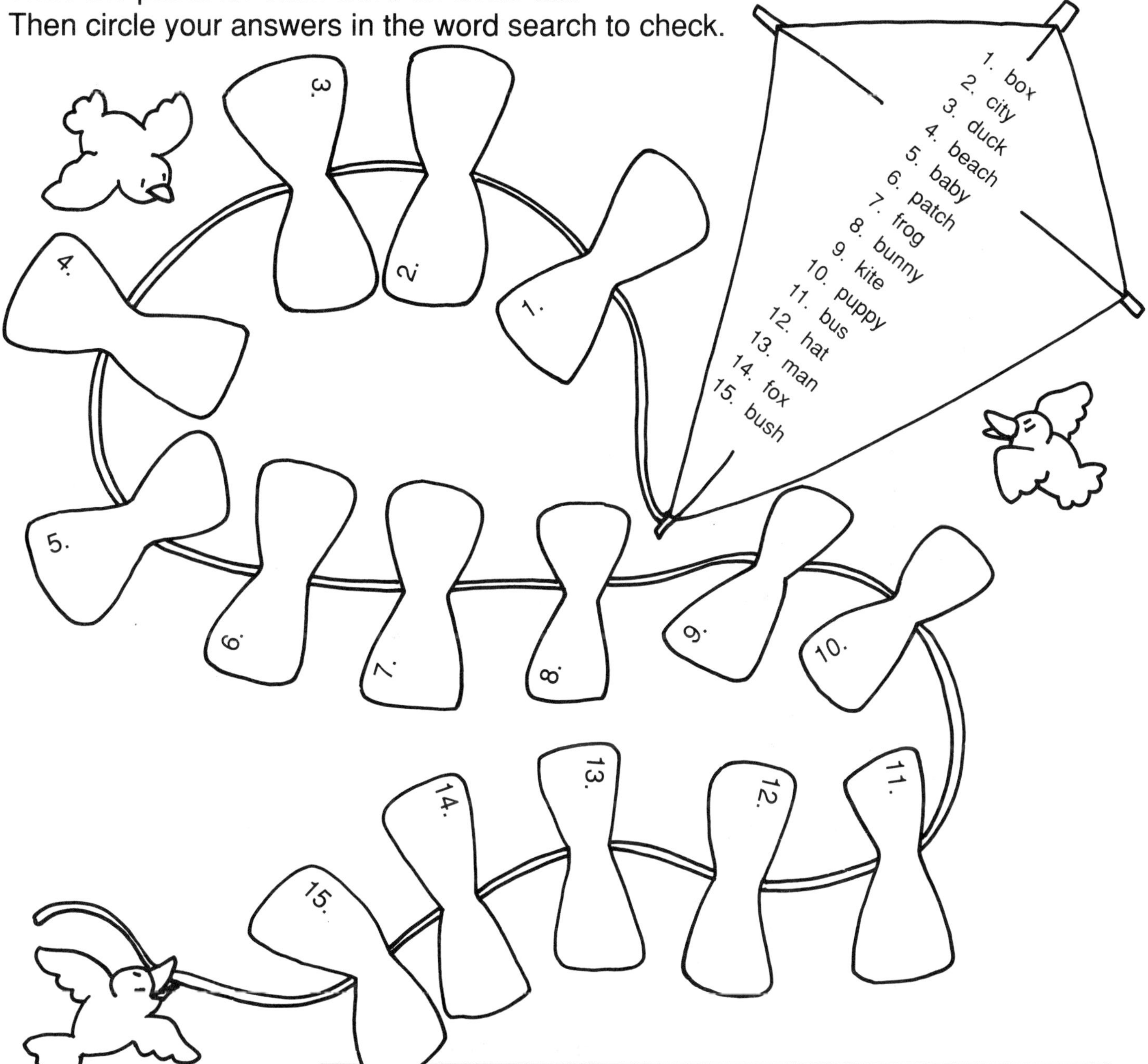

3.

2.

1.

4.

1. box
2. city
3. duck
4. beach
5. baby
6. patch
7. frog
8. bunny
9. kite
10. puppy
11. bus
12. hat
13. man
14. fox
15. bush

5.

6.

7.

8.

9.

10.

14.

13.

12.

11.

15.

I	L	F	C	J	P	A	T	C	H	E	S	A	V	G
Q	A	V	P	X	D	Y	B	U	N	N	I	E	S	D
D	K	B	U	B	U	H	A	T	S	B	O	X	E	S
R	H	O	M	U	C	R	B	E	A	C	H	E	S	A
F	O	X	E	S	K	K	I	T	E	S	F	T	T	O
W	B	M	N	H	S	W	E	C	I	T	I	E	S	D
N	E	S	Y	E	B	U	S	E	S	F	R	O	G	S
A	Z	T	O	S	C	P	U	P	P	I	E	S	F	W

Name _____

March Weather Record

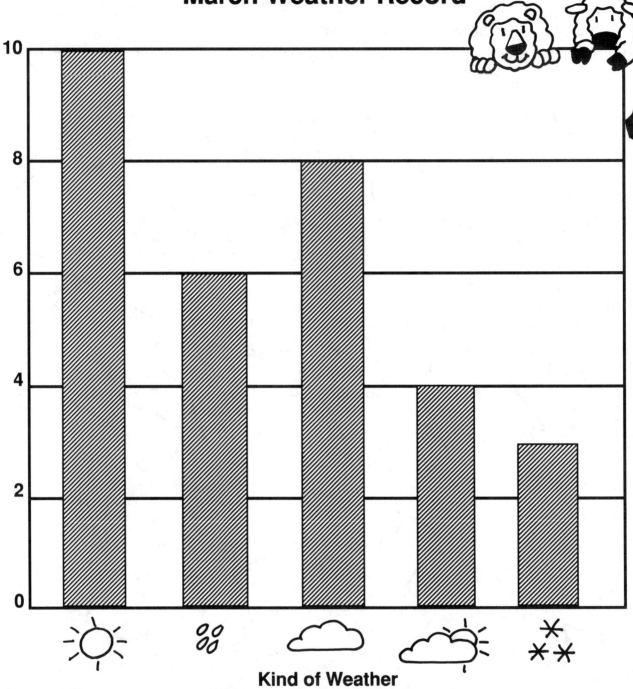

Kind of Weather

1. Write the number of days for each:

2. How many more days of rain were there than days of snow? _____

3. How many days were cloudy or partly cloudy? _____

4. Color the bars on the graph:
   red   black   blue   orange   yellow

Mrs. Roo's Spring Garden

Mrs. Roo wants to plant some tomatoes, but she doesn't know what to do first.
See if you can help her.
Cut on the dotted lines. Paste the correct signs in order.

| Have a bacon, lettuce, and tomato sandwich. | Buy some seeds at a garden shop. | Pull up weeds near the new plants. | Pick the tomatoes when they are red. | Plant your seeds in good, rich soil. | Water the seeds each day. |

Where do sheep go to get their hair cut?

To answer the riddle, solve the problems.
Write the letter of each problem in the correct blank below.
The first one is done for you.

(G) $ 2.69
   + 1.46
   $ 4.15

(T) $ 4.27
   + 3.73

(A) $ 6.84
   + 3.67

(H) $ 9.88
   + 6.43

(E) $ 4.59
   + 7.22

(O) $ 5.18
   + 3.75

(E) $ 7.87
   + 1.95

(A) $ 1.54
   + 0.96

(T) $ 4.36
   + 2.10

(H) $ 3.64
   + 0.17

(B) $ 7.08
   + 5.10

(H) $ 0.63
   + 0.29

(O) $ 3.82
   + 1.15

(Y) $ 7.42
   + 8.06

(A) $ 8.30
   + 4.87

(T) $ 3.95
   + 1.62

(O) $ 5.91
   + 2.18

(S) $ 4.83
   + 2.56

(A) $ 8.65
   + 0.29

(B) $ 6.10
   + 5.66

___ ___ ___ ___   G   ___   ___ ___   ___ ___ ___
$5.57 $3.81 $11.81 $15.48 $4.15 $8.09 $6.46 $8.93 $8.00 $0.92 $9.82

___ ___ ___ - ___ ___ ___   ___ ___ ___ P!
$12.18 $10.51 $8.94 $11.76 $13.17 $2.50 $7.39 $16.31 $4.97

Name _____

Spring Has Sprung!

Write a verb in each flower.
Use the word bank.
Color the flowers.

past tense verb—**yellow**
present tense verb—**purple**

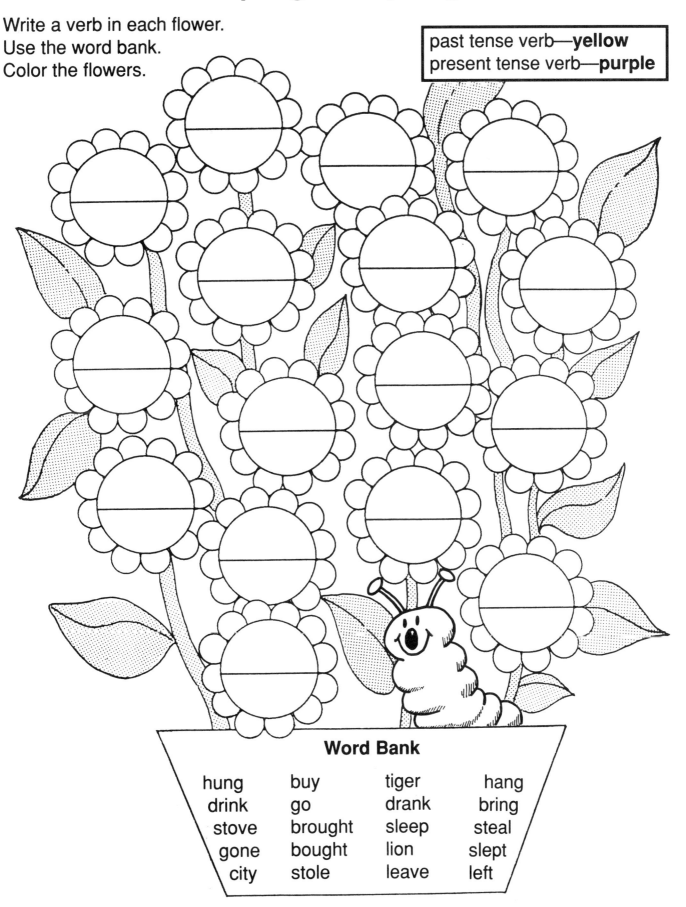

Word Bank

hung	buy	tiger	hang
drink	go	drank	bring
stove	brought	sleep	steal
gone	bought	lion	slept
city	stole	leave	left

Our Fine-feathered Friends

Spring is in the air—and so are all the beautiful birds that fascinate young and old. Capitalize on your students' interest in these winged wonders with the following activities and reproducibles. Before you know it, your whole class will be chirping with new information about birds, their habits, and their habitats.

Your Basic Bird

Compare pictures of birds. Make a chart for young children listing these basic bird characteristics:
- All birds have feathers.
- All birds have wings, but not all can fly.
- All birds hatch from eggs.
- All birds have bones and are warm-blooded.

Share some interesting bird trivia:
- The penguin uses its wings as flippers to swim.
- Many bird bones are hollow. This reduces weight and makes flying easier.
- Birds have higher body temperatures than mammals. They eat a lot because their bodies use up energy faster.
- The smallest bird is the bee hummingbird.
- Big birds live longer than most small birds. Parrots can live to be 70!

Beautiful Birds

There are over 8,600 kinds of birds, and ornithologists are discovering new species every year. Birds live in many habitats from jungles to deserts, from cities to ice floes. They nest in trees, on roofs, on the ground, and on mounds of mud in shallow lakes.

Go on a nature walk to look for evidence of birds. Ask students to bring in magazine and newspaper articles about birds. Display the pictures on a "Beautiful Birds" bulletin board along with plastic sandwich bags containing bits of eggshell or small feathers found in nature.

Pattern

_____
student

is now an
**Official
Member**
of the
**Bird-Watchers'
Club**

_____
date

Bird-Watchers' Club

Bird-watching is a popular hobby. Invite a local bird-watcher or wildlife naturalist to speak to the class about birds and migration. Show slides or pictures of local birds and point out some special features of each. Birds can be identified by color, size, kind of nest, behavior, and distinctive call. Provide a field guide in the classroom for quick reference.

As a class project, have students observe several different types of birds over a five-day period. Discuss good bird-watching techniques such as being quiet and keeping at a distance so as not to disturb the birds. You may want to make simple bird feeders to attract birds using the ideas on page 99.

Duplicate the bird-watch chart (on page 106) for each student to record his bird observations. (Younger students may draw pictures of the birds they saw.) When charts are completed, present students with membership badges for the Bird-Watchers' Club.

Feasts For The Feathery Ones

Spring is a wonderful time to put out bird feeders. Birds not only love birdseed, but also peanut butter, suet, bread, and even pancakes! Choose from the following feeders and have your students help our feathery friends.

- Spread a pinecone with peanut butter and roll it in birdseed. Tie a string to the pinecone and hang it from a tree branch. Delight your youngsters by mentioning that the string is likely to become nesting material in some bird's nest.
- Stuff a plastic strawberry basket with a mixture of suet and birdseed. Suspend the basket using string.
- Carefully poke floral wire through a rice cake for a hanger before spreading each side with peanut butter. Sprinkle birdseed atop the peanut butter. Use the floral wire to hook the feeder to a tree limb.

Protect Our Birds

Read a brief story or biography of John James Audubon to students. Discuss his contributions to our knowledge of birds of America. The National Audubon Society, one of the oldest and largest conservation organizations in North America, was named after this great naturalist and painter. The Audubon Society has been active in protecting birds through legislation and by establishing bird refuges.

Discuss what a bird sanctuary is and why it is necessary. Have children make banners telling the benefits of birds. Display the banners in the hall.

Building A Nest

A nest can be fascinating to young children, especially if it's situated so that they can observe its construction and use. Ask your youngsters what nests are made of, how birds make them, and what holds them together. Then read aloud *A First Look At Bird Nests* by Millicent E. Selsam and Joyce Hunt.

In preparation for making their own nests, have students take a nature walk for the purpose of collecting nesting materials. Dry grass, twigs, pieces of thread, string, pine straw, old fabric pieces, and shredded cotton make great nests. For each child's nest you will need: a paper bowl, glue, and nesting materials. Have each child spread a thick layer of glue on the bottom of the bowl and cover the glue with nesting materials. Allow these nests to dry overnight. Then have each student fill the inside of his nest with soft materials (such as cotton or feathers) as if preparing a soft place to lay eggs. As a follow-up to this activity, ask your students to compare how they made nests to how birds must do it.

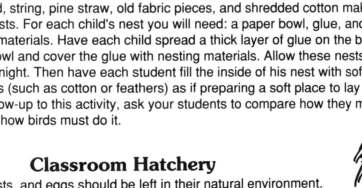

Classroom Hatchery

Most birds, nests, and eggs should be left in their natural environment. Stress the importance of leaving egg-filled nests alone. Since children are naturally curious about the hatching process, hatching eggs in the classroom can be an invaluable experience. Check with an agricultural extension office for assistance and information. Borrow an incubator and obtain some 18-day chicken eggs. Follow the instructions carefully, and the eggs will hatch in just three or four days.

Birds

Flying High

Most—but not all—birds fly. And while children can hop like frogs, run like dogs, and crawl like bugs, it is not that easy to fly! As an alternative to the real thing, have your children imagine what it would be like to fly. Darken the room, and ask your children to close their eyes and imagine they are birds in flight. Play background music such as Hap Palmer's "Sea Gulls" from *Music For Rest And Relaxation* or "Birds" from *Learning Basic Skills Through Music, Volume 1.* Or, from *The Carnival Of Animals,* play "The Swan" by Saint-Saëns. Read from *Flocks Of Birds* by Charlotte Zolotow to help students with visualization. Afterwards ask for volunteers to describe their "flights."

I Like Birds

Red birds,
Blue birds,
Yellow birds,
I like birds.

Flying birds,
Singing birds,
Nesting birds,
I like birds.

Bright birds,
Feathery birds,
Baby birds,
I like birds.

Winged Poetry

Your students can create a poem that appeals to the eyes as well as to the ears. Begin by cutting several sponges into bird shapes. Provide several pie tins, each containing a small amount and different color of tempera paint. Have students take turns dipping the sponges into the paint and onto a five-foot length of bulletin board paper, overlapping the designs. When the paper is dry, write on it with marker as your students dictate a poem in the format shown. Assist students in composing the poem so that the first stanza contains three lines that describe the appearances of birds. The second stanza should have three lines that describe birds' actions. And the final stanza should have three lines that describe birds' appearances. End each stanza with the line, "I like birds."

Centers Are For The Birds, Too!

Create bird-themed centers during your bird studies. Use the bird, egg, and nest patterns on page 101 to make a limitless array of centers. For example, have students match birds labeled with math facts to nests labeled with answers. Or number each of ten nests and provide 55 egg cutouts. Have students fill each nest with the appropriate number of eggs.

For the skill practice your students need—from homonyms to addition—these versatile patterns make it easy.

Flighty Fiction

Wrap up your unit on birds with some flighty creative writing. Provide story starters such as: *If I were a bird…, If I could fly…,* or *Hatching from an egg is like….* For fun, enlarge the bird pattern on page 101 and have students write their stories on the shapes. (Younger students can dictate while you write their stories for them.) Encourage your youngsters to let their imaginations fly!

If I were a bird, I'd fly to my grandmother's house every day. I'd eat cookies with Grandma. Then I'd fly home in time for supper.

Use patterns with "Centers Are For The Birds, Too!" on page 100.
Use the bird with "Flighty Fiction" on page 100 and "Foraging Feathered Friends" on page 102.

Spring Is For The Birds!

Fill a springtime bulletin board with bright birds and student writings. Attach real branches to your board. Have students cover small milk cartons with paper to make birdhouses to hang from the branches. Next have children draw, paint, and cut out pictures of birds to perch in the branches. Attach student-written poems, stories, and reports about birds to the display.

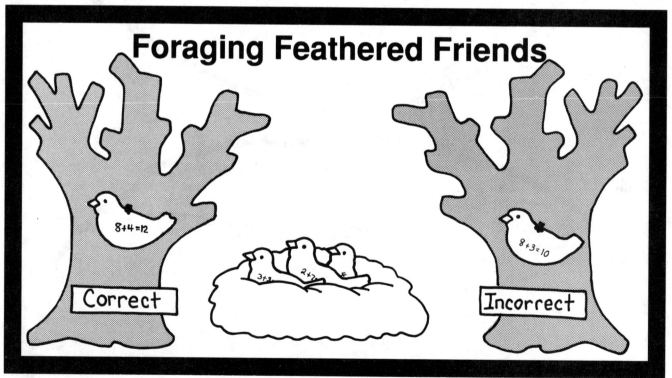

Foraging Feathered Friends

Your students will flock to this display to fill its bare branches with fine-feathered friends. Cut out two trees from butcher paper and mount on the board. Pin "Correct" and "Incorrect" labels to the trees as shown. Duplicate the bird pattern on page 101 on colorful construction paper. After laminating and cutting out the birds, use a permanent marker to label them with incorrect/correct spelling words or math problems. Store the birds in a construction paper nest stapled to the board as a pocket. Students pin each bird to the appropriate tree. To reprogram the birds for another skill, wipe clean with nail polish remover.

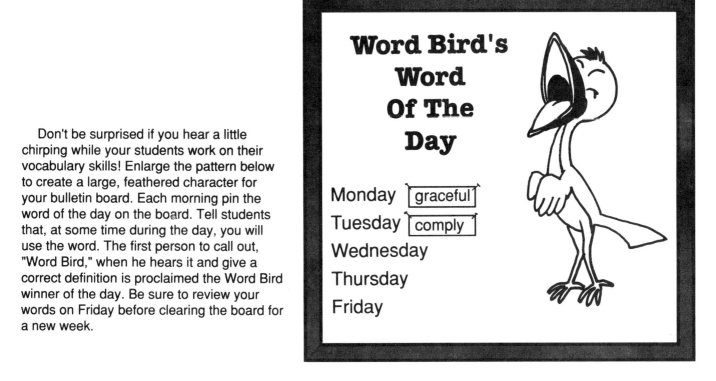

Don't be surprised if you hear a little chirping while your students work on their vocabulary skills! Enlarge the pattern below to create a large, feathered character for your bulletin board. Each morning pin the word of the day on the board. Tell students that, at some time during the day, you will use the word. The first person to call out, "Word Bird," when he hears it and give a correct definition is proclaimed the Word Bird winner of the day. Be sure to review your words on Friday before clearing the board for a new week.

Pattern

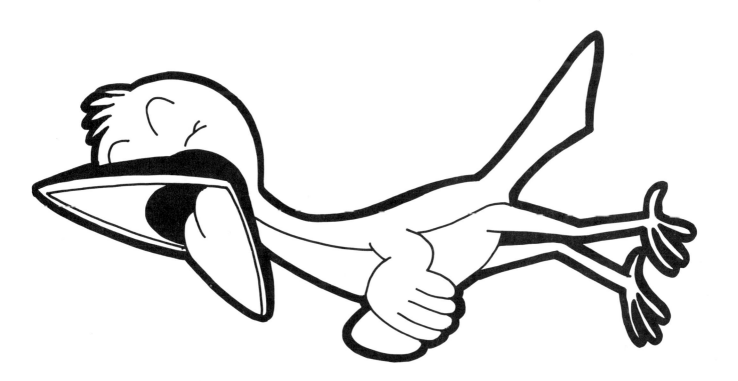

Fine-feathered Art Activities

Tape penny here.

Little Birds

For a quick afternoon art project, make these colorful birds. Cut out a 2" x 6" and a 1 1/2" x 6" strip of colored construction paper. Roll the strips into cylinders; then glue them together to make the head and body. When the pieces dry, cut out and color a pair of paper feet and wings, and a beak and tail (see patterns below). Fold back each piece along the dotted line and glue to the cylinders. Fringe or curl the tail of your bird to "ruffle his feathers." To help the bird stand upright, tape a penny inside the body cylinder at the bottom.

Fantasy Birds

Using scraps of metallic or brightly colored wrapping paper, children can create their own fantasy bird feathers. Give each child a piece of 18" x 24" construction paper for the background. Have each child draw and cut out a simple bird from a contrasting color of construction paper to glue to his background. Encourage children to think big and add their feathers, bits of fabric trim, sequins, and wiggle eyes to their birds. After birds are designed, have children write or tell stories about their creations. Ask each student to give his bird a name and tell if it is helpful or harmful, where it lives, what it eats, and any interesting behavior he observed.

My bird is a cockajoo. It lives in the jungle. It eats mosquitoes. It is helpful. It shakes its head a lot.

Patterns

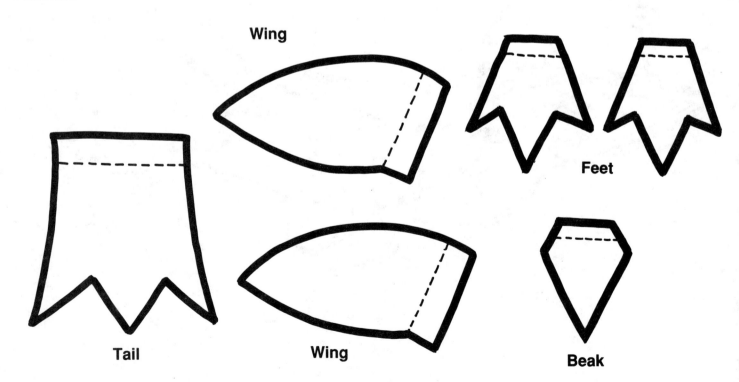

Wing

Feet

Tail

Wing

Beak

Name _____

Birds Of A Feather

Color the birds according to the code on the birdhouse.

WELCOME

_____ = Yellow

_____ = Blue

©1990 The Education Center, Inc.

Note To Teacher: Before duplicating, program the birds with incorrect/correct math facts, homonym/synonym word pairs, hard *g*/soft *g* words, etc. Fill in the code to match.

105

Name _____

106

My Bird-watch Chart

Name of Bird	Description: color, size, markings	Place and Date	Time of Day and Weather	Observations: habits, movements

Note To Teacher: See "Bird-Watchers' Club" on page 98.

Beaks And Bills

Birds use their bills and beaks to help them eat their food. Look at each bird's bill or beak. Match it with the food the bird eats. Trace over the bird's name.

cardinal

duck

hummingbird

eagle

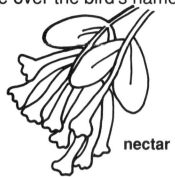

nectar

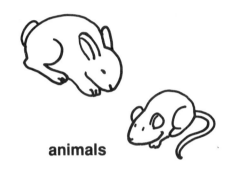

animals

water plants and animals

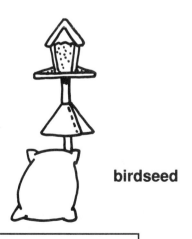

birdseed

Bonus Box: On the back of this paper, list five insects you think a bird might eat.

Healthy Foods Mean
Healthy Kids

March is National Nutrition Month, a terrific time to take a bite out of poor eating habits. Help your students eat their way to better health with the following ideas and reproducibles.

Balanced Meal Smorgasbord

Setting up a cafeteria serving line and selecting a balanced meal could give your students a new perspective on nutrition. In preparation for this activity, ask cafeteria workers to explain and demonstrate their work to your students. Have students determine some differences between cafeteria cooking and home cooking. What types of machines are used in the school cafeteria? Is the cafeteria manager careful to plan menus that contain all four food groups?

Ask students to cut out food pictures from magazines. Place the pictures on a table. Give each student a paper plate. Ask students to walk by the table as though it were a serving line, selecting foods for a balanced meal. After pasting the foods on their plates, have students label the foods by food group. Have students present their meals to the class. Discuss the appeal of each meal and its nutritional value.

The Big Four

Students can help make this file folder game to review the four basic food groups. Ask children to cut out pictures of individual foods from magazines. Provide oaktag cards on which students paste the pictures and label the foods. Laminate the cards. Label and mount four pockets inside the folder. Place the food cards in a string-tie envelope for storage and attach it to the folder. Students choose foods and place them in the correct pockets.

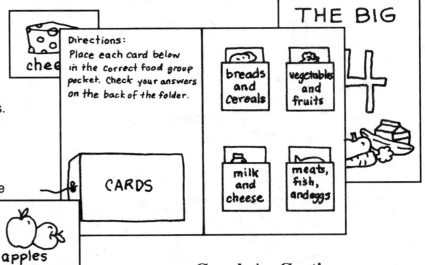

Graph Au Gratin

Students will analyze their breakfasts and improve their math skills with this before-school activity. Provide 4" x 5" pieces of paper and a bulletin board or large chart divided into four rows: one for each of the food groups. As they arrive, have students draw each item they ate for breakfast on a sheet of paper, then attach it to the chart.

When the graph is complete, have students analyze the results. Which is greater, the milk or the cereal group? How many servings of meat and milk were consumed? Try it again another day and compare the results. The math activities are limitless!

Ingredients À La Carte

Amaze your students by introducing them to the ingredients in the foods they eat. Encourage them to bring food labels and containers that would otherwise be discarded. Examine the ingredient lists together to determine the nutritional values of foods. Remind students that ingredients are listed in order according to quantity. What is the main ingredient? Is it sugar? What are the many names for sugar? How does the ingredient list of one brand compare to another? Creating a new awareness about ingredients could promote better nutritional habits among your students.

An Apple A Day

Colorful, apple-shaped diaries are an excellent starting point for examining students' eating habits. Duplicate the apple pattern on page 110 on red and white construction paper. Have each student cut out two red and five white apples. Using the red apples as covers, staple all seven apples together to make a booklet. Ask each student to write "My Diet" and his name on the front of the booklet. Then have him label the pages "Monday" through "Friday." As they note their diets for the week, ask students to categorize the foods according to the four food groups. Also have them list low-nutritional-value foods that they eat, such as carbonated drinks and chips.

Make a bulletin board showing four grocery bags and a trash can. Label the bags. From the students' booklets, list the foods your class consumed during the week. List the low-nutritional-value foods on the trash can. Discuss the results.

Chug, chug, toot-toot; off your youngsters go to learn about good nutrition! Divide your class into small groups and assign each group one of the four basic food groups. Have each group paste appropriate magazine pictures to the corresponding bulletin board train car. When your nutrition unit is over, reuse the train by replacing the cars with cars of picture words related to specific initial consonants or cars illustrating the four types of sentences. Add a new title.

Nutrition
Pattern

Use with "An Apple A Day" on page 109.

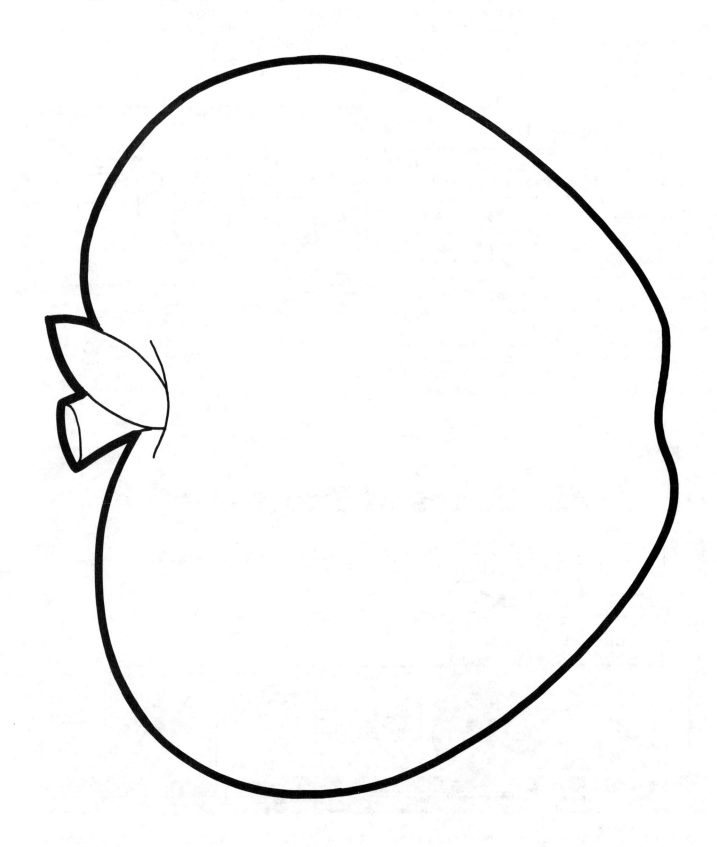

110

Name _____

Bag It!

Some nutritionists divide foods into seven groups instead of four. Write each food from the shopping list on the correct bag.

pork chops
onions
wheat bread
vanilla ice cream
bananas
hamburger buns
cream cheese
applesauce
tomatoes
oatmeal
skim milk
peanut butter
margarine
yellow squash
eggs
tangerines
rice cakes
grapefruit
broccoli
yogurt
lettuce
green beans
turkey
butter
peaches
green peas

Meat, Poultry, Fish, Eggs, Dried Beans and Peas, and Nuts

_____
_____
_____

Leafy, Green, and Yellow Vegetables

_____
_____
_____

Citrus Fruits, Tomatoes, and Salad Greens

_____
_____
_____

Potatoes and Other Vegetables, and Noncitrus Fruits

_____
_____
_____

Bread, Flour, and Cereals

_____
_____
_____

Milk and Milk Products

_____
_____
_____

Bonus Bag: Plan a meal using the foods on the list. Include one food from each group. Write your meal on the back of this sheet.

Butter and Fortified Margarine

_____
_____

Nutritious Facts And Figures

Use the chart to complete the statements below.

Food	Amount	Calories	Food	Amount	Calories
Apple	1 medium	80	Egg	1 large	82
Banana	1 small	81	Hamburger	4 oz.	260
Beans, green	1/2 cup	15	Ice Cream	1/2 cup	165
Bread, white	1-oz. slice	76	Lettuce	1 head	23
Bread, whole wheat	1-oz. slice	69	Milk, skim	1 cup	88
Cake, chocolate	1–2" wedge	288	Milk, whole	1 cup	159
Celery	1 stalk (8")	7	Pie, apple	1/8	302
Cheese, American	1-oz. slice	113	Popcorn	1 cup plain	23
Cookie (chocolate chip)	1 (2 1/4" diam.)	50	Potato chips	10	115

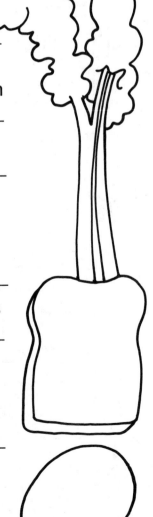

1. The chart lists foods in _____ order.

2. Which four foods listed have the fewest calories?
   _____
   _____

3. One apple, one banana, and _____
   have about the same number of calories.

4. Does white bread have more or less calories than
   whole wheat? _____

5. Two chocolate chip cookies have how many
   calories? _____

6. The food listed that has the most calories is
   _____.

7. Which has fewer calories: one cup of plain
   popcorn or 10 potato chips? _____

8. Does a slice of chocolate cake have more or less
   calories than a hamburger? _____

9. Skim milk has _____ fewer calories than
   whole milk.

10. If Jane ate an apple and Sally ate a slice of white
    bread, who consumed more calories? _____

Bonus Box: On a piece of art paper, design a bumper sticker with a
slogan promoting good nutrition.

©1990 The Education Center, Inc. • Key pp. 126–128

A Butterfly Collection

Butterflies are among the most beautiful of insects. Plan a beautiful classroom display with butterfly art. Encourage science observation, creative writing, and divergent thinking with these activities and worksheets.

How To Raise Butterflies In Captivity

The process of *metamorphosis* provides an excellent opportunity for scientific observation and record keeping over a three-week period. It takes a week to 12 days for caterpillars to complete their development. At this point, they hang upside down and shed their furry coats to become chrysalides. Each chrysalis must hang undisturbed during this pupal stage. In seven to ten days, the butterflies emerge. They pump blood through their veins to make their wings unfold and spread to full size. The wings harden in an hour or two, and the butterfly is ready to fly! Have students draw and label the stages in a butterfly's life.

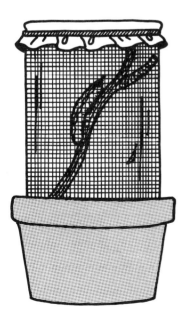

Caterpillar Cages

A suitable cage for caterpillars may be made using a clay flowerpot (eight or ten inches in diameter), wire screen, lightweight fabric or netting, a branch, and potting soil. Put some soil in the flowerpot to hold a sturdy branch. (The branch will provide support for the insect when it is time to pupate.) Form a cylinder of the screen and put the bottom edge in the soil so caterpillars cannot escape. Use the fabric or netting to make a lid on the cylinder. Tie the lid down carefully so that it can be removed daily to add fresh leaves and take out the old ones. The soil can be sprinkled with water, but it should never be soggy and wet.

Larvae or pupae collected in the autumn may develop only after exposure to winter temperatures. Cages should be placed in an unheated garage or porch. Conditions on a windowsill vary greatly so this is not a recommended location. The results of taking the necessary precautions are worth the trouble!

Butterflies

Caterpillar Capture

If caterpillars or pupae are brought into the classroom from home, be sure to supply the proper diet. A caterpillar of a certain species may feed exclusively on one type of foliage. Provide the type of vegetation on which the caterpillar was feeding at the time of capture. Fresh foliage should be supplied daily for voracious caterpillars. If you don't know what kind of caterpillar you have, consult a butterfly field guide. You may also get helpful information from your County Agricultural Extension agent and your State Department of Conservation.

Caterpillar Cabanas

As temporary homes for caterpillars or other little critters, make these quick and easy-to-store cages. Each cage is made of two inexpensive, round, metal cake pans and a piece of window screen or hardware cloth. Stack the cake pans and flatten the screen for off-season storage.

Butterfly Fact Box

This project can extend over several days or weeks as students learn new facts about butterflies. Decorate a tissue box with butterfly print gift wrap or stickers—or find a box already printed with butterflies. Provide small strips of paper for students to write butterfly facts that they discover in their research. Each fact should be restated in the student's own words with the reference cited. On the other side of the paper, the student writes a question that could be answered by his fact. Completed fact slips are placed in the box.

As a class review on a rainy day, share the questions. Divide the class into teams. Team captains take turns drawing a question and reading it to the opposing team. Teams earn one point for each correct answer. Use this same idea to review other subjects or topics.

Stained-Glass Butterflies

Duplicate two butterfly patterns on page 116 on dark construction paper for each child. Provide old crayons, plastic knives, waxed paper, scissors, glue, yarn or string, an iron, and an old towel to place under the waxed paper. Have children follow the instructions to make beautiful butterflies to hang in the windows or from the ceiling.

Chase away the winter doldrums with this colorful display. Cut butterfly shapes in graduated sizes from brightly colored construction paper. Glue three butterfly cutouts together at the center, creating a three-dimensional look, and decorate as desired. To complete the butterflies, students write butterfly stories, poems, or reports, and display them from the butterflies' centers. Let students make additional springtime decorations to complete the board.

Creative Writing With Butterflies

Use this chart to compare creative writing to the stages in the life of a butterfly. Display it as a reminder of how to develop good paragraphs. Write the following story starters on colorful, cut-out butterflies and mount them on a bulletin board. Each child chooses a butterfly and follows the steps to complete the story. Provide butterfly-shaped paper for final drafts.

When I was just a little caterpillar, I had fun…
When I get out of this chrysalis, I'm going to…
Being a monarch butterfly means I get to go to Mexico for the winter!
My cousin, Marvin Moth, asked me to go out with him one night…
Oh, no! Here comes Mr. Jones again with his butterfly net!
The contestants in the Butterfly Beauty Pageant fluttered on stage…

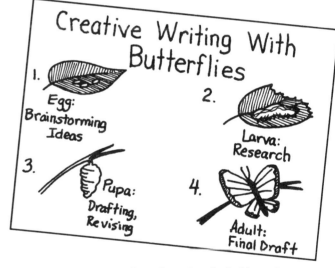

Fluttering Adverbs And Adjectives

Stretch students' vocabularies with words that describe butterflies. Have each student trace or draw a butterfly on his paper. Ask children to write adverbs for each letter in the word *butterfly* on one wing. On the other wing, they write adjectives. Allow the use of a dictionary. When wings are completed, have students use the descriptive phrases to write poetry.

B—bountifully beautiful
U—utterly unique
T—totally tireless
T—terribly terrific
E—extraordinarily exotic
R—really regal
F—flawlessly fluttering
L—literally lovely
Y—youthfully yearning

115

Stained-Glass Butterflies

Use with "Stained-Glass Butterflies" on page 114.

Student Instructions:
1. Cut out butterflies on all solid lines.
2. Shave crayon bits onto the waxed paper using a plastic knife or pencil sharpener.
3. Cover the shavings with another piece of waxed paper. Iron the papers together so crayon shavings melt.
4. Glue one butterfly cutout to the colored waxed paper. Trim excess waxed paper.
5. Match up the second butterfly and glue to the other side so waxed paper is sandwiched between the butterflies.
6. Attach a piece of yarn or string to hang.

116

Splashes Of Color

Moths and butterflies are a very large group of insects. There are about 90,000 varieties. They all have one thing in common: scaled wings. The thousands of tiny scales on each wing produce the wonderful colors that we see. To get a closer view, have students examine the wing of a moth or butterfly under a microscope.

Children will enjoy creating colorful moth or butterfly pictures. Have each child fold a piece of white construction paper. On the crease, place three blobs of tempera paint. Each blob should be a different color and about 1/8 of a teaspoon of paint. The student refolds his paper and gently rubs from the fold outward in the shape of wings. Open the paper to let it dry. When the paintings are dry, children add details with markers. (Butterfly antennae have knobs on the ends, while moth antennae end in a point and are usually hairy or feathered.) Cut out the insects and mount for an eye-catching display.

Beautiful Butterflies

It may be difficult for children to believe that the graceful butterfly was once a fuzzy caterpillar. The four stages of a butterfly's life are the same for all butterflies; however, the duration of each stage varies. Explain how these insects change through a process called *metamorphosis*. Have each child fold a blank piece of paper into fourths. In each box, he draws a stage in the life of a butterfly and adds a caption. Instruct students to cut the boxes apart and trade with a friend. Partners try to reassemble the pictures in a cartoon strip, then trade back to check.

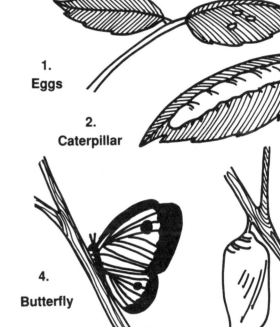

**1.
Eggs**

**2.
Caterpillar**

**4.
Butterfly**

**3.
Pupa**

Butterfly Wings

Your students will jump into this butterfly project with both feet. To make a butterfly, trace the outlines of both of your shoes onto construction paper and cut them out. Transform the foot cutouts into wings by gluing them to a black construction paper butterfly body as shown. Glue on pipe cleaner antennae.

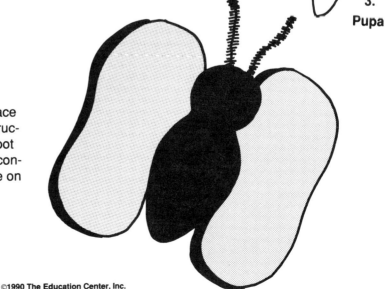

Name _____

A Butterfly Collection

Note To Teacher: Use this sheet for student reports or creative writings about butterflies. Or list ten tasks on the sheet and have students color a butterfly for each task they complete. For a parent newsletter, white-out the title and add "Fluttering By With Class News" to the top.

A Butterfly's Life

**A caterpillar hatches from an egg.
It makes a chrysalis.
Then it turns into a butterfly.**

egg

1

caterpillar

2

chrysalis

3

butterfly

4

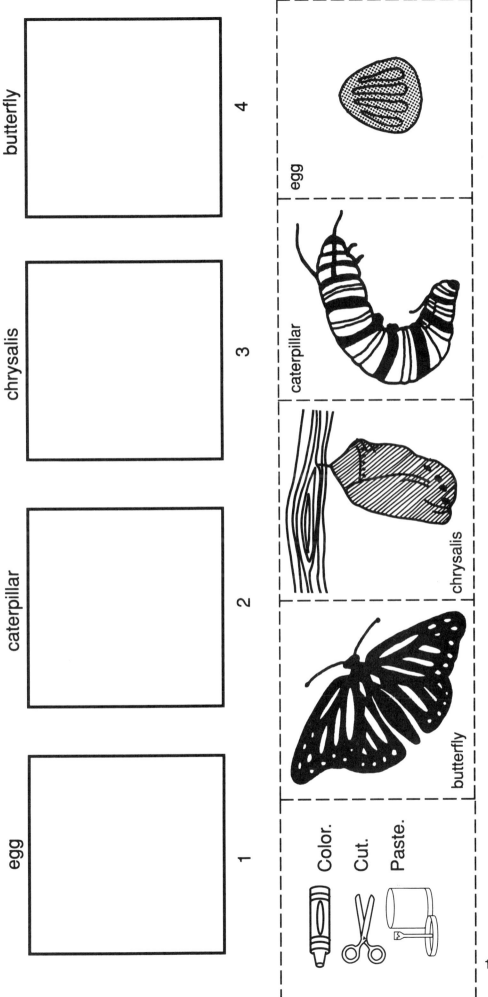

egg

caterpillar

chrysalis

butterfly

Color.

Cut.

Paste.

©1990 The Education Center, Inc.

Caught In The Net!

On the back of this sheet, write each group of words in alphabetical order to make a sentence.

1. butterflies   valley   gracefully   fly   beautiful   the   over

2. definitely   world   butterflies   our   grace

3. crawl   can   more   us   caterpillars   miles   many   than

4. tirelessly   with   crawl   wiggling   zeal   caterpillars

5. upon   insects   plants   do   many   trek   like   to

6. like   are   moths   butterflies   primarily

7. us   nature   wondrous   with   works   provided

8. flourish   bright   the   tropics   butterflies   in

9. information   toward   keeps   reaching   gathering   wisdom   man

10. can   everyone's   butterflies   delight   world

NOW write two alphabetical sentences of your own.
Scramble the words.
Give them to a friend to unscramble!

Bonus Box: What makes a butterfly different from a moth? Make a poster showing the differences between these two insects.

Origami Butterflies

The Japanese have made an art of folding paper. They call this art *origami.* Follow these instructions to make two origami butterflies. Color your butterflies and attach them to a branch or piece of paper.

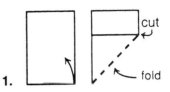

1.

1. Begin with a square piece of paper. If your paper is not square, fold the bottom edge as shown so it matches the adjoining side. Cut off the excess paper that extends above the top edge of the folded portion. See diagram 1.

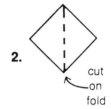

2.

2. Cut the square in half on the diagonal fold. Each triangle can be used to make a butterfly. See diagram 2.

3.

3. Fold the triangle in half as indicated by the dotted line and arrow in diagram 3.

4. Cut in 1/3 of the length of the fold as shown in diagram 4.

4.

5. Fold back the wing as indicated by the dotted line and arrow. Fold one wing only. See diagram 5a.

6. Turn over the butterfly and fold the other wing using the procedure in step 5. Your butterfly should look like diagram 5b.

5a.

7. To make antennae, cut small slivers from the front edges of the wings, leaving them attached near the butterfly's body. Cut both antennae at the same time and taper them so they are narrower at the edge of the wings and wider near the body.

5b.

8. You can make the butterfly's antennae curl by gently pulling along them with your thumbnail. See diagram 6.

6.

9. Make your second butterfly following the same steps.

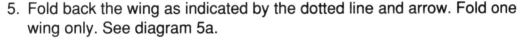
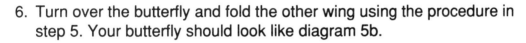

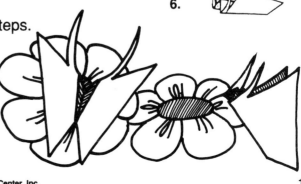

Name _____

122

No Moths Allowed!

Find the five moths which have gotten mixed into the butterfly jar.
Do your work carefully on another piece of paper.

1. If 67 – 23 = 44, cross out the pearly eye.

2. If 85 – 12 = 73, cross out the California sister.

3. If 49 – 25 = 25, cross out the white-veined dagger.

4. If 94 – 32 = 52, cross out the chain-spotted geometer.

5. If 86 – 54 = 32, cross out the question mark.

6. If 78 – 42 = 36, cross out the Harris' checkerspot.

7. If 35 – 14 = 29, cross out the yellow woolly bear.

8. If 63 – 20 = 43, cross out the broken dash.

9. If 57 – 25 = 32, cross out the clouded sulphur.

10. If 79 – 66 = 13, cross out the Olympian marble.

11. If 86 – 40 = 46, cross out the mourning cloak.

12. If 54 – 23 = 37, cross out the black witch.

13. If 62 – 22 = 40, cross out the great purple hairstreak.

14. If 98 – 55 = 63, cross out the elegant sphinx.

black witch

California sister

clouded sulphur

elegant sphinx

great purple hairstreak

Harris' checkerspot

broken dash

chain-spotted geometer

mourning cloak

Olympian marble

pearly eye

question mark

white-veined dagger

yellow woolly bear

Bonus Box: Create your own original butterfly or moth. Draw a picture of it and give it a name. Write several sentences under your picture explaining how the insect got its name.

TOOTHPASTE

Black History Month

Answer Key

Page 14

F	1.	Fruit does not have enough sugar to hurt your teeth.
T	2.	Tooth decay can be hazardous to your health.
F	3.	You should replace your toothbrush only when the bristles fall out.
T	4.	Flossing daily is good for your teeth.
F	5.	You shouldn't worry about a small hole in your tooth.
T	6.	Every person grows two sets of teeth.
T	7.	Molars are for grinding food.
T	8.	If you can't brush after a meal, you should at least rinse with water.
T	9.	Once tooth decay starts, only a dentist can stop it.
T	10.	Incisors are for tearing food.
F	11.	You should hold a toothbrush with two hands.
T	12.	The root holds a tooth in place in the gums.
T	13.	Your permanent teeth are your second set.
F	14.	If you brush your teeth carefully, you don't need to floss.
T	15.	You'll have fewer acid attacks on your teeth if you eat sweets only at mealtime.
F	16.	A good way to remove plaque is to eat a piece of celery.

Page 17

1. always
2. far
3. found
4. soft
5. low
6. thin
7. smile
8. worst
9. sell
10. dirty
11. sweet
12. wet
13. tiny
14. quiet
15. sad

Page 19

4	If the groundhog does not see his shadow and stays outside, warm weather is coming.
1	People gather to watch the groundhog on February second.
3	Then he looks for his shadow.
2	The groundhog comes out of his hole.
5	But if he sees his shadow, the groundhog will run back into his hole.
6	This means we will have six more weeks of cold weather.

Page 40

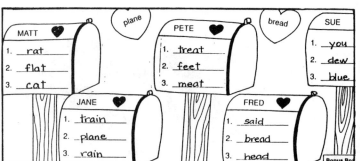

MATT
1. rat
2. flat
3. cat

plane

PETE
1. treat
2. feet
3. meat

bread

SUE
1. you
2. dew
3. blue

JANE
1. train
2. plane
3. rain

FRED
1. said
2. bread
3. head

Bonus Bo...

Page 42

27 +19 = 46	34 +26 = 60	25 +27 = 52
63 +28 = 91	42 +29 = 71	18 +38 = 56
56 +25 = 81	19 +44 = 63	32 +58 = 90	16 +19 = 35
27 +48 = 75	33 +49 = 82	25 +39 = 64	17 +54 = 71	29 +58 = 87
17 +57 = 74	35 +58 = 93	39 +19 = 58	26 +28 = 54	55 +26 = 81

Page 44

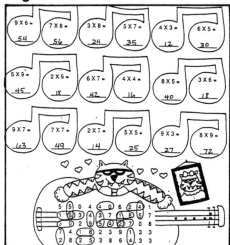

9 X 6 = 54	7 X 8 = 56	3 X 8 = 24	5 X 7 = 35	4 X 3 = 12	6 X 5 = 30
5 X 9 = 45	2 X 9 = 18	6 X 7 = 42	4 X 4 = 16	8 X 5 = 40	3 X 6 = 18
9 X 7 = 63	7 X 7 = 49	2 X 7 = 14	5 X 5 = 25	9 X 3 = 27	8 X 9 = 72

Page 50

1. martin luther king said, "i have a dream."
2. americans fought against each other in the civil war.
3. men and women were kidnapped from their homes in africa and brought to america as slaves.
4. george washington carver discovered over 300 uses for peanuts.
5. harriet tubman was a conductor on the underground railroad to canada.

Capitalize the first word in a sentence and the first word in a quotation. Also capitalize proper names and names of countries, continents, nationalities, and events.

Sentence	What did you underline?	Why?
1	- Martin Luther King - I	- proper name, first word in sentence - first word in a quotation
2	- Americans - Civil War	- first word in sentence, name of nationality - name of event
3	- Men - Africa - America	- first word in sentence - name of continent - name of country
4	- George Washington Carver	- first word in sentence, proper name
5	- Harriet Tubman - Underground Railroad - Canada	- first word in sentence, proper name - proper name - name of country

Page 51

1.	10 -5 = 5	2.	6 -3 = 3	3.	7 -4 = 3	4.	9 -7 = 2
5.	5 -0 = 5	6.	8 -2 = 6	7.	10 -1 = 9		
8.	7 -5 = 2	9.	9 -5 = 4	10.	6 -6 = 0		

126

Answer Key

Page 52
The answers are Marian Anderson, Duke Ellington, W.C. Handy, and William Still.

Page 60
The **long o** words are:

hope	soap
bone	snow
old	bowl
rose	nose
cold	grow
know	go
coat	

Page 61

1.	Born in a log cabin in Hardin County, Kentucky	A	(O)
2.	Rode a horse or ferry to school every day	(N)	C
3.	Favorite pastime was reading	D	(V)
4.	Became a lawyer	S	(H)
5.	Traveled through wild country to survey land	(R)	U
6.	Led an army in the Revolutionary War	(E)	N
7.	Spoke out against slavery	L	(I)
8.	Helped United States gain freedom from England	(O)	F
9.	Known as the "Father Of Our Country"	(S)	M
10.	Was president during the Civil War	A	(C)
11.	Was assassinated in 1865	P	(I)
12.	Face found on the penny	W	(R)
13.	Face found on the quarter	(O)	G
14.	Was our first president	(R)	E

George Washington had lost nearly all of his own teeth by the time he was 57. What were his false teeth made from?

R H I N O C E R O S   I V O R Y
14 4 7 2 13 10 6 12 1 9   11 3 8 5

Page 75

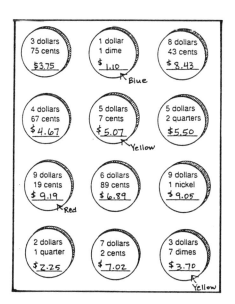

Page 76

Page 93

1. boxes		9. kites	
2. cities		10. puppies	
3. ducks		11. buses	
4. beaches		12. hats	
5. babies		13. men	
6. patches		14. foxes	
7. frogs		15. bushes	
8. bunnies			

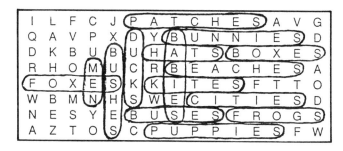

Page 94

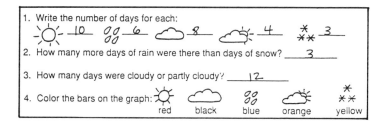

1. Write the number of days for each:
☀ 10 ☂ 6 ☁ 8 ⛅ 4 ❄ 3
2. How many more days of rain were there than days of snow? 3
3. How many days were cloudy or partly cloudy? 12
4. Color the bars on the graph: ☀ red ☁ black ☂ blue ⛅ orange ❄ yellow

Page 95
1. Buy some seeds at a garden shop.
2. Plant your seeds in good, rich soil.
3. Water the seeds each day.
4. Pull up weeds near the new plants.
5. Pick the tomatoes when they are red.
6. Have a bacon, lettuce, and tomato sandwich.

Answer Key

Page 96

(G) $2.69 + 1.46 = $4.15	(T) $4.27 + 3.73 = $8.00	(A) $6.84 + 3.67 = $10.51	(H) $9.88 + 6.43 = $16.31	(E) $4.59 + 7.22 = $11.81
(O) $5.18 + 3.75 = $8.93	(E) $7.87 + 1.95 = $9.82	(A) $1.54 + 0.96 = $2.50	(T) $4.36 + 2.10 = $6.46	(H) $3.64 + 0.17 = $3.81
(B) $7.08 + 5.10 = $12.18	(H) $0.63 + 0.29 = $0.92	(O) $3.82 + 1.15 = $4.97	(Y) $7.42 + 8.06 = $15.48	(A) $8.30 + 4.87 = $13.17
(T) $3.95 + 1.62 = $5.57	(O) $5.91 + 2.18 = $8.09	(S) $4.83 + 2.56 = $7.39	(A) $8.65 + 0.29 = $8.94	(B) $6.10 + 5.66 = $11.76

T H E Y   G O   T O   T H E
$5.57 $3.81 $11.81 $15.48 $4.15 $8.09 $6.46 $8.93 $8.00 $0.92 $9.82

B A A - B A A   S H O P!
$12.18 $10.51 $8.94 $11.76 $13.17 $2.50 $7.39 $16.31 $4.97

Page 107

cardinal—birdseed
duck—water plants and animals
hummingbird—nectar
eagle—animals

Page 111

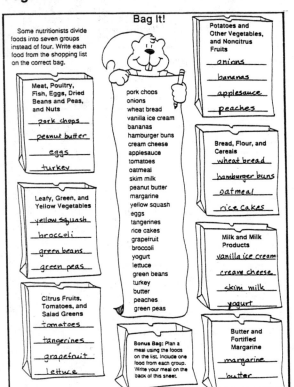

Page 112

1. alphabetical
2. celery, green beans, lettuce, popcorn
3. one egg
4. more calories
5. 100 calories
6. apple pie
7. popcorn
8. more calories
9. 71
10. Jane

Page 120

1. Beautiful butterflies fly gracefully over the valley.
2. Butterflies definitely grace our world.
3. Can caterpillars crawl many miles more than us?
4. Caterpillars crawl tirelessly wiggling with zeal.
5. Do insects like many plants to trek upon?
6. Are butterflies like moths primarily?
7. Nature provided us with wondrous works.
8. Bright butterflies flourish in the tropics.
9. Gathering information keeps man reaching toward wisdom.
10. Butterflies can delight everyone's world.

Page 122

The five moths are the black witch, the elegant sphinx, the chain-spotted geometer, the white-veined dagger, and the yellow woolly bear.